CW01084639

Rheumatoid Arthritis Diet Cookbook

Charles Thompson

Copyright© 2020by Charles Thompson

All rights reserved. This document is geared towards providing exact and reliable information with regards to the topic and issue covered. The publication is sold with the idea that the publisher is not required to render accounting, officially permitted, or otherwise, qualified services. If advice is necessary, legal or professional, a practiced individual in the profession should be ordered. - From a Declaration of Principles which was accepted and approved equally by a Committee of the American Bar Association and a Committee of Publishers and Associations. In no way is it legal to reproduce, duplicate, or transmit any part of this document in either electronic means or in printed format. Recording of this publication is strictly prohibited and any storage of this document is not allowed unless with written permission from the publisher. All rights reserved. The information provided herein is stated to be truthful and consistent, in that any liability, in terms of inattention or otherwise, by any usage or abuse of any policies, processes, or directions contained within is the solitary and utter responsibility of the recipient reader. Under no circumstances will any legal responsibility or blame be held against the publisher for any reparation, damages, or monetary loss due to the information herein, either directly or indirectly.

Respective authors own all copyrights not held by the publisher. The information herein is offered for informational purposes solely, and is universal as so. The presentation of the information is without contract or any type of guarantee assurance. The trademarks that are used are without any consent, and the publication of the trademark is without permission or backing by the trademark owner. All trademarks and brands within this book are for clarifying purposes only and are the owned by the owners themselves, not affiliated with this document.

Contents

Rheumatoid Arthritis Diet Cookbook

Introduction

Rheumatoid arthritis is a chronic systemic inflammatory disease that affects both small and large joints; these become painful, swollen, and deform over time. It can also involve other organs and systems such as the lung, eye, skin, kidneys, and blood vessels. Rheumatoid arthritis progression is variable, ranging from very mild or subclinical forms with spontaneous remission to rapidly progressing forms. Most patients present to the physician in an intermediate stage, with symptomatic episodes separated by periods of relative inactivity. In America, it affects 600/700 thousand people. Each year, there are about 10-20 new cases per 100,000 men and 20-40 new cases per 100,000 women, and it can occur at any age but is most common between the ages of 40 and 70. The peak of onset of the first symptoms occurs between the ages of 35 and 45. The triggering causes of arthritis are still not fully understood. However, it is impossible to speak of a hereditary disease even if there is a genetic predisposition to get sick (a first degree relative of a person with RA has a probability between 3 and 10 times greater than the general population to develop the same disease). To combat rheumatoid arthritis symptoms, it is essential to make the right changes to your lifestyle and diet.

Chapter 1: What is Rheumatoid Arthritis?

Rheumatoid arthritis is a chronic inflammatory autoimmune disease that attacks the joint tissues of a person whose immune system, instead of protecting the body from external agents such as viruses and bacteria, is abnormally activated against it. In this case, the antibodies hit our synovial membrane, the joint capsule's inner lining, which reacts to the inflammation by increasing in volume and giving rise to the synovial tissue. We speak of tenosynovitis, the inflammation that involves the tenosynovial sheath of the tendons. The growth of the synovial tissue causes progressive destruction of the cartilage, which in severe cases reaches the bones and other surrounding tissues, including tendons and ligaments. Rheumatoid arthritis mainly affects the small joints, such as hands and feet, but it can potentially involve every part of the body: in this case, we speak of systemic disease.

Arthritis or osteoarthritis?

Arthritis and osteoarthritis are conditions that affect the joints, and both fall into the category of rheumatic diseases; the symptoms are partly overlapping,

•ache,

•rigidity,

•movement restriction,

But the underlying causes of the two pathologies are quite different. Arthritis is an autoimmune inflammatory disease that can arise at any age, while arthrosis is a degenerative disease typical of the second half of life.

Causes

Rheumatoid arthritis is mainly a joint disease. The joint is the point where two or more bones come into contact. With a few exceptions (for example, the skull and pelvis), the joints are made to allow movement between bones and to absorb shocks caused by actions such as walking or repetitive gestures. The ends of a bone are covered with a strong, elastic tissue called cartilage. The joint is surrounded by a capsule that ensures protection and support. The joint capsule is aligned with a type of tissue, the synovium, which secretes synovial fluid, a transparent substance that lubricates and nourishes the cartilage and bones inside the capsule.

Like many other rheumatic diseases, RA is an autoimmune disease; the diction originates from the fact that the subject's immune system, in charge of defending the body from infections and diseases under normal conditions, attacks its own joint tissues for unknown reasons. Leukocytes (white blood cells), which are the cellular expression of the immune system, reach the synovium and cause inflammation (synovitis), which manifests itself with:

•heat,

•redness,

•swelling

•and pain,

•the typical symptoms of rheumatoid arthritis.

During the inflammatory process, the synovium, thin under normal conditions, thickens and swells the joint, making it soft and sometimes hot to the touch. As the disease progresses, the inflamed synovium invades and destroys cartilage and bone within the joint. The joint support and stabilization apparatus, therefore the surrounding muscles, ligaments, and tendons, weakens and is no longer able to perform its function. These effects determine the pain and joint damage often found in rheumatoid arthritis. Those who study rheumatoid arthritis currently believe that bone damage begins during the first or second year of the disease, which is one of the reasons why early diagnosis and treatment are so important.

Risk factors

The reasons why the immune system attacks its tissues in rheumatoid arthritis are not yet fully understood, but in recent years, scientific research has begun to bring together the factors involved.

Genetic (hereditary) factors: some genes, known for their role in the immune system, be associated with the tendency to develop rheumatoid arthritis. For related genes, the frequency of individual "risky" genes is only slightly higher in subjects with rheumatoid arthritis than in healthy controls. In other words, individually, a gene by itself carries only a relatively small risk of disease. Some individuals with these genes never develop the disease. These observations suggest that although the genetic makeup plays an essential role in determining the disease's possible development, it is not the only factor involved. Instead, many genes are involved in determining whether a person will develop the disease and its severity.

Environmental factors: many researchers think that there must be a triggering event to activate the disease in people genetically predisposed to rheumatoid arthritis. Various factors have been proposed, but a specific agent has not been identified.

Other: some think that hormonal factors also come into play, and this hypothesis derives from the observation that:
•Women are more at risk than men.
•The disease may improve during pregnancy and then flare up later.
•Breastfeeding can also worsen the disease.
•The use of contraceptive drugs can increase the risk of developing the disease.

This seems to indicate that hormones, or the possible deficiency or variation of some, may favor the disease's progression in genetically predisposed people exposed to environmental triggers. Even if there is no definitive certainty, one thing is sure: rheumatoid arthritis is the result of the interaction of several factors.

Symptoms

Rheumatoid arthritis mainly affects the joints. It can cause any joint problems, although the small joints in the hands and feet are often the first to be affected. Typically, the disease affects the joints symmetrically (both sides, with the same intensity and simultaneously), although this is not always the case.

The main symptoms affecting the joints are:

Pain: Joint pain associated with rheumatoid arthritis is typically described as stabbing and acute. Often, it is most intense in the morning and after a period of inactivity.

Stiffness: The joints affected by rheumatoid arthritis can be stiff. For example, when the hands are affected, it may not be possible to fully bend the fingers or close the hand into a fist. Like joint pain, stiffness is typically more severe in the morning or after inactivity. The morning stiffness associated with another form of arthritis, osteoarthritis, generally disappears about half an hour after waking up, while that linked to rheumatoid arthritis typically lasts longer.

Swelling, heat and redness: The joint surfaces affected by rheumatoid arthritis become inflamed, thus causing the joint to swell, which becomes hot and painful to the touch. In some people, the swelling takes on a strong character, resulting in so-called rheumatoid nodules, formations that develop under the skin around the diseased joints.

Other symptoms

In addition to joint problems, some patients with rheumatoid arthritis experience more general symptoms, such as:

•fatigue and lack of energy,

•temperature,

•sweating,

•loss of appetite,

•weight loss,

The inflammation associated with rheumatoid arthritis can sometimes cause problems in other parts of the body:

•dry eyes, if the eyes are affected,

•chest pain, due to the involvement of the heart or lungs.

Symptoms vary from person to person. They come and go and can change over time. There may be acute episodes when conditions deteriorate, and symptoms are more intense.

Complications

The evolution of rheumatoid arthritis varies from person to person. Some patients have mild or moderate forms, with periods of worsening or flare-ups and periods when they are better, remissions. Others suffer from severe forms of the disease, which are almost always active; arthritis lasts for several years or a lifetime and causes joint damage and severe disability.

Although rheumatoid arthritis is mainly a joint disease, its effects are not only physical. Many people face problems such as:

•depression,

•anxiety,

•sense of helplessness,

•low self-esteem.

The disease can affect virtually any component of a person's life, from work to family life. It can also interfere with family life's joys and responsibilities and hinder planning to procreation.

 Fortunately, current treatment strategies allow many people with the disease to lead active and productive lives. These strategies include pain relievers and therapies that slow joint damage, balance rest and exercise, and patient education and support programs. In recent years, research has provided new insights into the disease and has increased the likelihood of finding even better ways of treating the disease in the near future.

Some people with rheumatoid arthritis also have non-joint symptoms. Many patients develop anemia or reduced production of red blood cells. Less frequently, sufferers have neck pain and dry eyes and mouth. Finally, in some patients, we observe:

•carpal tunnel syndrome,

•widespread inflammation, which can affect

-lungs (with cough, shortness of breath, ...),

-heart (pericarditis),

-eyes (Sjogren's syndrome),

-blood vessels

•cardiovascular diseases (diabetes, high blood pressure, metabolic syndrome, atherosclerosis).

Chapter 2: Diet and lifestyle

As anticipated, rheumatoid arthritis is an idiopathic pathology that involves the activation of the immune system against the joint tissues. This means that there is currently no definitive cure, even if many behaviors have been observed that can improve symptoms and slow pathological progress; let's see which ones.

Lifestyle

Some activities can help improve a person's ability to function independently and maintain a positive attitude.

Rest and exercise: The patient with rheumatoid arthritis needs the right balance between rest and exercise: prevalence of rest when the disease is active, the prevalence of exercise when it is not. . Rest helps reduce active joint inflammation and pain, as well as being an antidote to fatigue. The duration of rest varies according to the subject; in general, frequent naps are more effective than long periods of bed rest. Exercise is also essential for keeping muscles healthy and robust, safeguarding joint mobility, and maintaining flexibility. Exercise can help you sleep better, reduce pain, maintain a positive attitude and a bodyweight within limits. Exercise programs should take into account individual physical abilities, limitations, and needs that change over time.

Joint care: In some subjects, the temporary use of splints around ailing joints reduces pain and swelling thanks to the splints' support and rest action. They are mainly used on the wrists and hands, but also on the ankles and feet. The choice of a splint and the verification of its adequacy can be made by a doctor, a physiotherapist, or an occupational therapist. Joint stress can also be reduced through self-help devices (such as zipper pulls, long-handled shoe horns), aids for getting up and sitting down from chairs, toilets, and beds, and changes in how the individual carries out his or her daily.

Stress Reduction: People with rheumatoid arthritis face emotional as well as physical difficulties. Feelings of fear, anger, and frustration, perceived by the illness, combined with any painful stimulus or physical limitation, can increase stress levels. Although there is no reliable data on whether stress plays a role in causing the disease, it can be more difficult to accept. Stress can also affect the amount of pain the sufferer feels. There are various effective techniques for managing stress. Regular rest periods can help, as can relaxation, distraction, or visualization exercises. Exercise programs, participation in support groups, and good communication with the health care team are other ways of reducing stress.

Climate: In some cases, arthritis tends to worsen when the weather changes abruptly, but there are no certainties on the possible action to prevent or reduce the effects of the disease exerted by specific weather conditions. Moving to a place with a different climate generally makes no long-term difference to the disease course.

Special diets, vitamin supplements, and other alternative approaches for treating rheumatoid arthritis have been suggested. Scientific research has shown that some of these, for example, fish oil-based supplements, can help reduce joint inflammation. Mostly, however, either no controlled scientific studies have been performed, or no particular benefits have been identified for these therapies.
As with any other treatment, the patient will need to discuss the doctor's benefits and limitations before starting any alternative or a new type of therapy. If the doctor considers the approach valid and not dangerous, the alternative may be part of the subject's treatment plan. However, it is important not to neglect traditional medical treatments.

Diet

It is still uncertain whether certain specific dietary measures have a genuinely positive effect; on the other hand, there is a real nutritional strategy to reduce joint inflammation.

Nutrition for arthritis: general guidelines

•Limit the consumption of nutrients that promote the inflammatory process (for example, arachidonic acid, as the body converts it into inflammatory prostaglandins) by reducing simple sugars and the overall consumption of fats;

•Increase the consumption of nutrients with anti-inflammatory action, such as Omega-3 polyunsaturated fatty acids, which inhibit the synthesis of inflammation mediators;

•Increase the intake of antioxidants such as vitamins A, C, and E and minerals such as zinc and selenium, as they act against free radicals and help counteract inflammation. A food that contains many of these protective nutrients is Parmesan which, in just 25 grams, provides 56 µg of vitamin A, almost 3 mg of zinc and 3 µg of selenium, as well as plenty of calcium and high biological value proteins that strengthen muscles and bones;

•Increase the intake of magnesium with the diet. This mineral helps to reduce muscle tension which worsens the perception of pain;

•Increase fiber consumption to maintain a good intestinal flora, as some scientific studies have linked intestinal dysbiosis with rheumatic diseases.

Nutrition for arthritis: which foods should I limit?

•Alcohol (including wine and beer). The increase in the frequency of alcohol consumption is associated with the severity of the disease (the more often you drink alcohol, the more the pathological condition can worsen), especially in the case of rheumatoid arthritis

•White sugar, cane sugar, honey, and sweeteners in the broad sense (e.g., syrups). To sweeten drinks (tea, coffee, etc.), if it is not possible to do without the sweet taste, natural or artificial sweeteners can be used;

•Sweets and sweets (ex: cakes, pastries, biscuits, puddings, snacks, ice creams, candies, jams, etc.);

•Fruit in syrup, candied fruit, fruit mustard;

•Sugary drinks and soft drinks, such as cola, tonic water, iced tea, but also fruit juices, because they naturally contain sugar (fructose) even if they say "no added sugar" on the package;

•Fatty seasonings such as butter, margarine

•Sausages

•Fatty meats such as games and offal.

Arthritis nutrition: what can i eat?

•Extra virgin olive oil, preferably raw to season food, and measuring it with a spoon to check the quantity. The nutrients of olive oil have natural anti-inflammatory properties;

•Fish (fresh or frozen), to be consumed no less than two to three times a week. Bluefish (sardines, anchovies, bonito, etc.), in particular, is an excellent source of Omega-3 polyunsaturated fats. Other fish very rich in Omega-3 are salmon, mackerel, tuna, trout, herring, and their derived oils;
•Nuts, in particular walnuts, almonds, and oilseeds such as flax seeds, hemp, etc. These foods also represent a very important source of Omega-3; however, due to their high caloric content, it is recommended to consume them daily but always controlled (nuts a day);

•Low-fat cheeses (ricotta, mozzarella, Spreadable cheese, etc.) or cheeses that contain less fat than the whole milk with which they are produced, such as Parmesan. This cheese is partially decimated during processing. Therefore it has less fat and is naturally lactose-free. Also, the fats of Parmesan are 28% monounsaturated (such as those of olive oil) and 4% polyunsaturated (such as those of fish and nuts);

•Raw and cooked vegetables to be taken in large portions (at least one at each meal) for the important contribution of vitamins, minerals, antioxidants, and fiber. Try to vary the quality (and therefore the colors) of the vegetables as much as possible, possibly choosing seasonal ones, to ensure a more generous supply of these nutrients effective against inflammation. Also, the fiber content is beneficial for maintaining a correct intestinal bacterial flora. Adequate amounts of magnesium can be found in artichokes, zucchini, broccoli, cabbage, and cauliflower;

•Fresh fruit (two to three servings a day), as it represents, together with vegetables, the primary source of antioxidants, vitamins, minerals, and fiber. Vary the color and quality of the fruit as much as possible to ensure a more excellent supply of all the nutrients capable of inhibiting the action of arachidonic acid and preventing damage caused by free radicals. The consumption of the peel is recommended to keep all the nutrients intact, of course, if edible and after washing it well with running water;

•Bread, pasta, rice, spelled, barley, and other complex carbohydrates, preferably derived from wholemeal flours. Thanks to their particular chemical composition, whole grains increase the intake of fiber and reduce the glycemic peak. The insulin produced in response to the glycemic peak increases eicosanoid production, i.e., derivatives of arachidonic acid. So pay attention to polished rice, rice flour, and refined cereals in general (everyday white bread, rusks, crackers, breadsticks, etc.) because they have a higher glycemic index and are to be consumed in small quantities;

•White meats (chicken, turkey, rabbit), recommended for the high protein content combined with low-fat content, or red meats but chosen in leaner cuts and deprived of visible fat. Meat is an excellent source of iron, an essential mineral in the treatment of rheumatic diseases as it can often lead to anemia;

•Spices and aromatic herbs to flavor dishes (even in place of salt). Among the spices, turmeric seems to have some reasonably useful anti-inflammatory properties in the early stages of rheumatic disease. As an alternative to spices, grated Parmesan (one-two tablespoons) can also be used to replace salt.

Nutrition for arthritis: practical advice

•In case of overweight or obesity, it is recommended to reduce weight and abdominal circumference, which indicates the amount of fat deposited viscerally. Waist circumference values greater than 94 cm in men and 80 cm in women are associated with a "moderate" cardiovascular risk; values higher than 102 cm in men and 88 cm in women are instead associated with a "high" cardiovascular risk. Remember that returning to a normal weight allows you to reduce the joints' overload and, therefore, improve the symptoms of rheumatic pathology. If you want to know how many calories you should eat per day and get balanced and personalized menus based on your daily nutrient requirement, download this weight control program for free;

•Not smoking. As with cardiovascular and oncological diseases, rheumatological diseases are also more common among those who are unable to give up this dangerous vice;

•Promote proper sun exposure to ensure adequate vitamin D production, a vitamin with a powerful anti-inflammatory effect unfortunately not present in food. It is useful to check the blood values (blood) to evaluate with your doctor any supplementation in case of insufficiency of this important micronutrient;

•Practice physical activity. It is advisable not to improvise and instead contact a Motor and Sports Sciences specialist to check which activity is most suited to your state of health and joint mobility: aerobics, free body exercises and/or in water, etc. In general, aerobic activity (e.g., walking, cycling, swimming, etc.) performed for a minimum of 150 minutes per week - ideally 300 - and muscle toning exercises practiced with method and regularity help to improve the functionality of the joints and check your weight. Furthermore, it is advisable to learn the correct posture of the various daily movements, such as lifting weights, sitting in front of the computer, etc., in order not to cause damage to the joints and muscles, but to subject them to the minimum effort;

•Never underestimate the alarm bells: some specific signs distinguish almost all rheumatic disorders, such as persistent joint and muscle pain, exhaustion and fatigue, stiffness, anxiety, and depression. Sufferers should go to a specialist. It is important to promptly report symptoms to your doctor to be able to treat the disease in the most appropriate manner and timing;

•Regularly carry out checks and blood tests while maintaining proper adherence to drug treatment and, if you have doubts about symptoms and complications, ask your doctor or rheumatologist for more information about the drugs (all this once the diagnosis of the rheumatic disease has been confirmed);

•In the case of intestinal dysbiosis, taking probiotics could help improve the condition.

Chapter 3: Breakfast

1) Donut with carob flour

Ingredients:
- **340 g of water**
- **90 g extra virgin olive oil**
- **320 g wholemeal flour**
- **70 g carob flour**
- **50 g of corn starch**
- **1 sachet of gluten-free yeast**
- **9 dates and 9 plums**
- **90 g 92% dark chocolate**
- **1 pinch of salt**

Sift the flour, carob flour, yeast, corn starch, and salt. Separately, blend the dates and plums with 140 g of water. Emulsify this mixture with the rest of the water and the oil. Combine the dry ingredients and create a soft dough. Cut the dark chocolate with a knife and add to the dough. Bake for about 40 minutes at 180 degrees.

2) Chestnut flour muffins

Ingredients:
- **500 g of chestnut flour**
- **3 apples**
- **Apple juice**
- **½ teaspoon of cinnamon**
- **1 pinch of salt**
- **sunflower oil**
- **½ teaspoon of cream of tartar**

In a bowl, mix the chestnut flour, salt, cream of tartar, and cinnamon. Gradually pour in the apple juice necessary for a soft batter. Add the washed and sliced apples. Stir one last time. Brush a muffin pan with a little oil. Distribute the mixture and bake at 180 degrees for about 25 minutes. Remove from the oven and let them cool before serving.

3) Radicchio and carrot muffins

Ingredients:
- **250 g of wholemeal flour**
- **1 carrot**
- **½ head of radicchio**
- **½ sachet of cream of tartar**
- **150 g of oat milk**
- **4 tablespoons of oil**
- **1-2 tablespoons of toasted linseed and sesame**
- **50 g of roasted peanuts**
- **1 pinch of salt**

Clean the radicchio, wash it and dry it, then cut it into thin slices. Wash the carrot and dry it, remove the ends and grate it. Gather the vegetables, seeds, and peanuts in a bowl. Separately, mix the flour with salt and yeast. Then add it to the bowl's contents, mix and gradually pour the milk and oil until you have a soft and creamy mixture. If it is too dry, add a little more oat milk. Pour the mixture into the appropriate cups and bake at 180 ° C for about 20 minutes. Serve the muffins warm or cold.

4) Apple and hazelnut tartlets

Ingredients:
- **200 g of hazelnuts**
- **200 g of almond flour**
- **100 g of powdered sugar**
- **250 g of peeled apples**
- **350 ml of water**
- **oil**

Finely chop the hazelnuts with the help of a food processor. Put them in a bowl and mix them with the lupine flour, icing sugar, and water. At this point, add the apples cut into small pieces and knead again, distributing the fruits evenly. Lightly oil the cake tins and arrange the mixture, leveling it well. Bake the cakes at 170-180 ° for about 35 minutes.

5) Biscuits with apples and cinnamon

Ingredients:
- **300 g of hazelnuts**
- **200 g of rice flour**
- **2 yellow apples**
- **180 g of honey**
- **2 eggs**
- **90 ml of oil**
- **2 tablespoons of brown sugar**
- **4 tablespoons of cinnamon powder**

Peel the apples, core them, and cut them into small pieces. Finely chop the hazelnuts with the sugar, mix them in a bowl with the rice flour, and then add the oil and lightly beaten eggs. Stir well and add the apples, honey, and cinnamon, mixing everything thoroughly. With your hands, form fairly large balls and flatten them slightly with your palms. Line a baking sheet with parchment paper and place the biscuits on it. Bake them in a preheated oven at 160 ° for 30-35 minutes. Once cooked, remove them gently from the pan and let them cool (in fact, when hot, they are very delicate and could break easily). Keep them in a closed container.

6) Smoothie with banana and tea

Ingredients:
- 1 banana
- almond milk
- 1 teaspoon of tea
- a few pinches of vanilla powder
- rice syrup

Peel the banana and cut it into small pieces. Put it in the glass of a hand blender or a mixer and mix until you get a puree. Add the tea, vanilla, and rice syrup and start the appliance again, adding enough almond milk to obtain a smooth and soft mixture. Drink it immediately.

7) Quinoa pancakes

Ingredients:
- 80 g of quinoa
- 50 g of chickpea flour
- 100 ml of water
- 1 onion
- 20 g of grated cheese
- salt
- extra virgin olive oil

Rinse the quinoa and boil it for about 15 minutes in double its volume of water. Turn off, put the lid on and leave it to rest for another 10 minutes. It will be cooked when the grains, from white, become a little transparent. Let it cool down. Clean the onion and cut it into slices. In a bowl, prepare a batter with water, chickpea flour, Parmesan cheese, and salt. Add the cooked quinoa to the batter. You will get a fairly solid dough. Heat a little oil in a pan and pour a spoonful of batter. In contact with the heat, the batter will spread to form pancakes. A soup spoon of batter equals a pancake. You can cook 4 or 5 at a time, depending on the size of the pan. Let the pancakes set for a couple of minutes, then turn them on the other side. Serve hot.

8) Oat, cocoa, almond and apple porridge with turmeric

Ingredients:
8-9 tablespoons of oat flakes
1 apple
2 teaspoons of cocoa powder
2 tablespoons of maple syrup
almond milk
5-6 shelled and peeled almonds
1 teaspoon of turmeric
1 tablespoon of rice syrup
1 pinch of salt
1 pinch of vanilla powder

Put the oat flakes in a bowl. Pour in the almond milk to cover them abundantly. Let it rest in the refrigerator overnight. The next morning, peel the apple and cut it into pieces. Transfer it to a saucepan with turmeric, rice syrup, salt, and vanilla. Stir and place on the stove. Dilute the mixture with a little water to prevent it from sticking. Cook for a few minutes, until it is soft but avoiding it becoming a puree; the fruit pieces must remain intact. Remove from the heat and set aside. Take the oat flakes from the refrigerator; add the cocoa powder and maple syrup, stirring well. If necessary, dilute with more milk. If you prefer a lukewarm porridge, heat it in a saucepan over low heat for a couple of minutes. In this case, it will be necessary to add even more milk. Complete with cooked turmeric apples and chopped almonds.

9) Wholemeal bread croutons with soy, figs and chocolate

Ingredients:
- 1 slice of wholemeal bread
- soy sauce
- 1 dried fig
- dark chocolate
- Maple syrup

Lightly toast the bread. Then spread it with an amount of soy as you like. Spread the fig cut into small pieces or slices on top. Sprinkle with maple syrup and complete with the chopped dark chocolate. Eat immediately.

10) Caramelized pear cake

Ingredients:
- 300 g of shortcrust pastry
- 1 kg of pears
- 75 g of whole cane sugar
- 3 tablespoons of sunflower oil
- lemon juice

Wash, peel and cut each pear into eight pieces and sprinkle with lemon to prevent blackening pears. Roll out the shortcrust pastry, sprinkle the bottom of a cake mold with sugar, add the oil slowly and arrange the pear slices in a spiral. Lay the pastry sheet on top of the pears and tuck it up along the edges. Make a hole in the center of the cake to allow the steam to escape during cooking. Bake for 15 minutes in a hot oven (200 °) and 25 minutes in a medium oven (150-170 °). As soon as it is out of the oven, turn the cake upside down on a serving plate.

11) Lemon biscuits

Ingredients:
- **2 cups of whole wheat flour**
- **2 cups of almond flour**
- **3/4 cup corn oil**
- **a pinch of salt**
- **the grated rind of 3 lemons**

For the dough's excellent result and speed up the times, it is good to use cold water and work the dough as little as possible. Combine the flours, salt, and peel of 3 lemons in a bowl, pour in the center the oil and enough water to obtain a thick dough. The dough should be rolled out immediately and roughly cut into diamond shapes to obtain many irregular biscuits. Bake in a hot oven at 200 degrees for 10 minutes. As an alternative to lemon zest, orange peel can be used. They are simple cookies, which can also be enriched with raisins, walnuts, and almonds.

12) Light pancake

Ingredients:
- 100 g of egg whites
- 125 g of Greek yogurt
- 80 g of wholemeal flour
- 2 tablespoons of honey
- 2 tablespoons of skim milk
- 1 tablespoon of seed oil
- 1 teaspoon of baking powder for cakes
- 1/4 teaspoon of baking soda
- 1/2 vanilla bean

TO SERVE
- honey
- blueberries or other fruit to taste

To make the light pancakes, first, collect the egg whites in a bowl. Beat them with a hand whisk for 30 seconds. Add the Greek yogurt, vanilla seeds, honey, and oil. Work everything until you get a homogeneous cream. Add the wholemeal flour, sifted with baking powder and baking soda, and mix it by slowly adding the milk. You will need to obtain a smooth and homogeneous batter with a slightly thick but not too thick consistency. Grease a non-stick pan with the seed oil and heat it well, removing the excess oil with kitchen paper. Pour a ladle of batter and let it spread out into a disc. When you notice large bubbles appear on the surface, turn the pancake and continue cooking on the other side. When cooked, transfer to a plate. Proceed in this way until the batter is used up. Serve the light pancakes warm with honey and blueberries.

Chapter 4: Single course

1) Rice with walnuts

Ingredients:
- 300 g of brown rice
- 600 ml of vegetable broth
- 2 cloves of garlic
- 1 small bunch of parsley
- 2 tablespoons of grated Parmesan cheese
- 30 g of light butter
- 40 g of shelled walnuts
- salt

Put the rice in a saucepan with 600 ml of broth, cover, and boil. Lower the heat and cook for about 20 minutes until the liquid runs out. Meanwhile, finely chop the garlic and parsley and chop the walnuts. As soon as the rice is cooked, add salt, season with the butter, and melt the latter. Add the prepared mixture, sprinkle with the walnuts and Parmesan cheese and serve.

2) Savoy cabbage and chickpea flan

Ingredients:
- 1 cabbage of about 800 g
- 4 medium potatoes
- 1 carrot
- 400 g of cooked chickpeas
- 1 teaspoon of curry
- 1 teaspoon of dry dill
- 4 tablespoons of oil
- 4 soy sauce
- salt

Remove 10 outer leaves from the cabbage, wash and blanch quickly in a little water. Drain and set aside. In the same water, blanch the potatoes cut into medium thickness slices for 5 minutes. Put these away too. Wash the rest of the cabbage and dry it, then chop it. Mix it in a saucepan with the curry, dill, and a little salt. Pour a few tablespoons of cooking water and cook over medium heat. After a few minutes, add the grated carrot, and after another 5 minutes, the coarsely chopped chickpeas with a blender. Turn them well in the sauce, pour a ladle of the cooking water, and cook for 5 minutes over high heat. When the liquid has evaporated, turn it off. Season with half the oil and season with salt. Arrange half of the cabbage in a pan lined with baking paper. Cover with half of the potatoes and sprinkle with half of the soy sauce. Now spread the chickpea mixture, cover with the last cabbage leaves and finish with the potatoes. Salt lightly and bake for about 40 minutes at 185 °. At the end, season with the oil and the soy sauce and serve.

3) Baked pasta with vegetables and ricotta

Ingredients:
- 160 g of wholemeal spelled pasta
- 200 g of ricotta
- 1 yellow pepper of 200 g
- 200 g of cherry tomatoes
- 200 g of zucchini
- 2 tablespoons of oil
- 1 tablespoon of olives
- 1 teaspoon of capers
- fresh oregano
- salt

Clean the pepper, removing seeds and white, then wash it; rinse and trim the zucchini, rinse the cherry tomatoes. Thinly slice the vegetables and brown them in a pan with the oil, olives, and capers. Meanwhile, boil plenty of salted water, add the pasta and drain it halfway through cooking. Mix it with the prepared dressing, add the ricotta and the chopped oregano. Stir well and distribute everything in a pan. Gratin the pasta for 10 minutes in the oven and serve it hot.

4) Fennel flans

Ingredients:
- **1 kg of fennel**
- **2 eggs**
- **1 shallot**
- **3 tablespoons of ground cashews**
- **½ tablespoon of fresh dill**
- **½ teaspoon of fennel seeds**
- **1 teaspoon of turmeric**
- **bread crumbs**
- **3 tablespoons of oil**
- **salt and pepper**

Clean the fennel, wash and halve it; steam them for 10 minutes. Transfer them to a bowl and mix with the chopped shallot and dill, the crushed seeds, turmeric, salt, and pepper. Let them cool, and then blend them by immersion. Add the cashews, beaten eggs, almost all the oil, and breadcrumbs needed to compact the mixture a little. Grease 6 single-portion molds with the remaining oil and sprinkle them with breadcrumbs. Transfer the fennel mixture and level it well. Bake at 180 degrees for about 30 minutes. Serve the flan hot directly into the molds.

5) Zucchini stuffed with quinoa

Ingredients:
- 10 medium zucchini
- 150 g of cooked quinoa
- 100 g of boiled chickpeas
- 70 g of almonds
- 15 pitted black olives
- a few leaves of basil
- a few mint leaves
- 1 handful of rocket
- 1 clove of garlic
- 2 tablespoons of breadcrumbs
- salt and pepper
- oil

Tick the zucchini and cut them in half lengthwise. Dig them, being careful not to break them, and set the pulp aside. Blanch them in salted boiling water for 3 minutes, then gently place them in a greased pan. Chop the chickpeas with olives, rocket, basil, mint, and almonds in a blender. Fry the garlic with a drizzle of oil, add the inside of the chopped zucchini, and cook for 10-15 minutes. Allow to cool, then mix in a bowl with the chickpea mixture and quinoa. Stuff the zucchini with the mixture. Sprinkle with breadcrumbs, season with a drizzle of oil, and bake for 15 minutes.

6) Wholemeal pasta with pea and caper cream

Ingredients:
- **280 g of short wholemeal pasta**
- **6-7 handfuls of fresh peas**
- **1 handful of salted capers**
- **1 clove of garlic**
- **2 handfuls of almonds**
- **1 handful of fresh parsley**
- **4-5 fresh basil leaves**
- **4-5 tablespoons of oil**
- **the juice of ½ lemon**
- **freshly ground black pepper**
- **sea salt, to taste**

Soak the salted capers in water for 10-15 minutes and then drain, rinse them once more, squeeze them well and chop them. Take the almonds, peel, and chop them. Blanch the peas in boiling water for 6-7 minutes. When they are tender, prepare the pea cream by blending them with the cleaned and dried parsley, some of the basil leaves, the peeled garlic, the oil, the lemon juice, and a few pinches of salt. Blend until creamy consistency. At this point, cook the pasta in plenty of boiling salted water and drain it at the cooking time indicated on the package. Season and toss the pasta with the pea cream, adding a drizzle of oil if necessary. Complete with capers, chopped almonds, freshly ground pepper to taste, a few basil leaves, and serve.

7) Rice and broccoli flan

Ingredients:
- 1 broccoli (about 600 g)
- 900 ml of soy milk
- 200 g of brown rice
- 300 g of cooked lentils
- Vegetable bechamel
- 1 1/2 tablespoons of flour
- 2 onions
- 2 shallots
- 2 carrots
- 1 sprig of rosemary
- 1 teaspoon of tomato paste
- bread crumbs
- 3 tablespoons of oil
- salt

Combine the rice and 400 ml of soy milk in a saucepan. Salt lightly, cover, and bring to a boil. Lower the heat and cook until the liquid runs out. Wash the broccoli and peel it, then steam it or boil it in water. Heat the remaining milk and add a little salt. Lightly toast the flour in a pan. Pour in the milk gradually, always stirring until you have a thick sauce. Put a few tablespoons in the rice, stir and let it cool. Meanwhile, prepare the vegetable sauce. Finely chop the onions, carrots, rosemary, and shallots in a blender, transfer them to a pan, cover them with a ladle of water in which you have diluted the concentrate, and let them dry over low heat for 10 minutes, adding a little water when needed. Salt lightly and cook for another 5 minutes, finally add the lentils. Lightly grease an ovenproof dish. Sprinkle it with breadcrumbs and line it with the broccoli florets. Pour a layer of béchamel, half of the rice, compacting it well with a spoon, the vegetable sauce, another layer of béchamel, the remaining rice, which you will press as above finally the rest of the sauce.

Bake at 190 degrees for about 40 minutes. Let the flan cool, then remove it from the mold and serve seasoned with the remaining oil.

8) Pasta and chickpea soup

Ingredients:
- **150 g of dried chickpeas**
- **120 g of wholemeal short pasta**
- **200 g of turnip greens**
- **2 cloves of garlic**
- **3 tablespoons of extra virgin olive oil**
- **120 g of tomato puree**
- **800 ml of vegetable broth**
- **1 bunch of aromatic herbs**
- **chilli powder**
- **salt**

Soak the chickpeas for 8-10 hours in plenty of water. Then drain and bring them to a boil in a pot with enough water to cover them. Cook them for an hour and a half, removing the foam that forms. Salt them only at the end. When the chickpeas' cooking comes to an end, peel the garlic and chop it finely; brown it gently in a saucepan where you have heated the oil. Then add the tomato puree, the aromatic bunch cleaned and tied with kitchen string, the turnip greens washed, peeled, and cut into strips, finally the legumes that are now ready. Let it cook for a few minutes, then add the vegetable broth and, as soon as it starts to boil, pour in the pasta, lightly salt, and cook for 10 minutes. Sprinkle with the chili powder and serve the soup hot.

9)   Pasta with broccoli, red onion and apples

Ingredients:
- 400 g of wholemeal penne
- 300 g of steamed broccoli
- 1 red onion
- 1 red apple
- 4 tablespoons of balsamic vinegar
- extra virgin olive oil
- salt

Cut the onion and sauté it in a pan with a drizzle of oil; add the balsamic vinegar, a little hot water, and the apple, de-cored and diced. Cook for 3-4 minutes, stir in the broccoli and add salt. Boil the penne in boiling salted water for the necessary time, drain and add them to the prepared sauce; mix well and finish with a drizzle of oil before serving.

10) Crispy meatloaf with mushrooms

Ingredients:
- 200 g brown rice
- 150 g hazelnuts
- 25 g dried mushrooms
- 2 sticks of celery
- 1 clove of garlic
- 100 g of corn starch
- 1.5 l of vegetable broth
- 1 handful of sesame seeds
- 1 handful of poppy seeds
- 3 tablespoons of oil, salt to taste

For the sauce
- 300 g red onions
- 2 bay leaves
- a little vegetable broth or hot water, salt to taste

Soak the mushrooms in lukewarm broth for 15 minutes. In a saucepan greased with oil, toast the rice with the chopped hazelnuts, celery, and chopped garlic. Pour in the broth and continue cooking for about 40 minutes. Then add the mushrooms to the rice, mix well and add the sifted corn starch a little at a time to avoid lumps. Let it cool, leaving the mixture to rest for 10 minutes. Meanwhile, preheat the oven to 180 °, put the mixture in a bowl (like a plum cake) lined with baking paper. Sprinkle the surface with sesame and poppy seeds and a drizzle of oil. Bake for 30 minutes. Prepare the sauce by stewing the onions with two cups of broth and the bay leaf; cook slowly until it reaches a sauce's consistency. Serve the meatloaf slices on a bed of onion sauce.

11) Pumpkin rolls

Ingredients:
- **200 g of pumpkin already peeled**
- **30 g of corn starch**
- **100g of ricotta**
- **30 g of pitted olives**
- **black sesame, oil, salt and pepper**

Cut the pumpkin into chunks, steam it for 10 minutes. Once cooled, blend it finely, add the starch, two tablespoons of oil, salt, and pepper. Mix the mixture; place 1 tablespoon between two sheets of greased parchment paper and press evenly with a spatula to obtain a disc of about 11 cm in diameter and 2 mm thick. Repeat the operation with the rest of the preparation until you have 8 discs. Bake them at 200 °; after 3 minutes, remove the upper leaves and continue cooking for 5-7 minutes. Chop the olives, add them to the ricotta, mix, salt, and pepper. When they are cold, carefully remove the pumpkin discs, cover them with the filling, leaving the edges free, and wrapping them around themselves. Brush them with oil on the surface and decorate with a little black sesame.

12)

Spaghetti in tofu cream with spinach and hazelnuts

Ingredients:
- **350 g of wholemeal spaghetti**
- **200 g of fresh spinach**
- **80 g of hazelnuts**

For the olive tofu cream
- **200 g of natural tofu**
- **the juice of half a lemon**
- **1 cup of capers**
- **1 cup of olives**
- **a large tuft of chopped parsley**
- **3 tablespoons of olive oil**
- **a tablespoon of soy sauce**
- **a pinch of salt**
- **1 small clove of garlic**

Put the water on the fire to cook the pasta; once it reaches a boil, add salt and throw the wholemeal spaghetti. In the meantime, take a saucepan with a little water and put it on the stove: as soon as it boils, add a pinch of salt and dip the natural tofu block cut into small pieces. Boil for a minute, drain, and put it in the blender, where you will add the olives without the stones, the sprig of parsley, the capers, the juice of half a lemon, the clove of garlic, the oil, the soy sauce, and the pinch of salt. To soften, you can add a few tablespoons of the tofu boiling water. Blend until you get a soft and homogeneous cream that you will keep aside. Then wash the fresh spinach leaves; you can roughly cut them or leave them whole. Dry them and keep them aside. Then take a non-stick pan and toast the hazelnuts, coarsely chopped. Drain the pasta and put it in a large bowl, and add the tofu cream to the olives; if necessary, help yourself with a little tofu cooking water, as above. Add the fresh spinach leaves, toasted hazelnuts, and finally a drizzle of raw oil. If you wish, you can also add a splash of fresh oregano or paprika powder. Serve the spaghetti hot and steaming. Simple and tasty!

Chapter 5: Snacks, appetizers and side dishes

1) Lentil bread

Ingredients:
- **250 g of cooked lentils**
- **200 ml of soy milk**
- **200 g of wholemeal bread**
- **1 teaspoon of paprika**
- **1 onion**
- **1 tablespoon of chopped parsley**
- **2 tablespoons of oil**
- **salt**

Heat the milk; add the paprika, mix well and pour on the chopped bread. Let the mixture rest for about 10 minutes. Meanwhile, finely chop the onion and put it in a pan with the oil and 2 tablespoons of water. Add the parsley and fry over medium heat, stirring occasionally. Let the excess liquid evaporate and turn off the heat. Gather the soaked bread, the fried onion, and the lentils in a blender. Blend them until you have a homogeneous mixture and season with salt. Turn on the oven to 190 ° C. Line a rectangular mold with parchment paper and turn the mixture upside down, leveling it evenly. Bake at 190 degrees for 20-25 minutes. Let the bread rest briefly in the oven, remove it and let it cool before turning it out. Slice it and serve it with a sauce.

2) Crunchy and spicy chickpeas

Ingredients:
- **250 g cooked chickpeas**
- **5 g cumin powder**
- **5 g dry ginger powder**
- **8 g fine whole salt**
- **10 g rice flour**

Mix the spices, salt, and the powders . Put the chickpeas in a bowl and pour the mix. Using your hands, mix everything together so that the flour and spices stick to the chickpeas. Preheat the oven to 200 ° C. Place the chickpeas on a baking dish covered with baking paper. Bake for 20 minutes or until crisp.

3) Eggplant croquettes with buckwheat

Ingredients:
- **2 Egg plants**
- **1 large boiled potato**
- **70 g of cooked buckwheat**
- **50 g of grated Parmesan cheese**
- **1 egg**
- **150 g ricotta**
- **1 tablespoon of oregano**
- **4 slices of wholemeal bread**
- **oil and salt**

Wash the eggplants, halve them, cut into the pulp, and cook in the oven for about 30 minutes until soft. Let them cool and squeeze them to remove excess water, then peel them. Mix them with the mashed potato with a fork, buckwheat, ricotta, parmesan, egg, oregano, and salt. Form many small balls the size of a large walnut and roll them in the bread without the crust and crumbled; finally, brown them over high heat with a drizzle of oil. Serve hot.

4) Cold pizza with soy mayonnaise, mozzarella and rocket

Ingredients:
- **300 g of rice flour**
- **100 g of wholemeal flour**
- **20 g of fresh brewer's yeast**
- **300 g of mozzarella**
- **1 pack of tomato puree**
- **200 g of rocket**
- **200 g of soy mayonnaise**
- **oil and oregano**
- **salt and pepper**

Mix the two flours on a pastry board and make a fountain. Dissolve the brewer's yeast in a glass with a little warm water and pour it into the center of the fountain. Gradually add 240 ml of warm water, incorporating it with the help of a fork, then flour your hands and knead the ball of dough until it is smooth and dry. Cover with a clean cloth and let rise. The ball of dough must be well swollen. In the meantime, cut the mozzarella into cubes and let it marinate in oil, salt, pepper, and oregano so that it tastes well. Preheat the oven to maximum temperature. Do not use the ventilated mode. When the dough has risen, roll it out in a 35x35 cm square pan well greased with oil. Spread the sauce on the surface with salt and a drizzle of oil. Bake until the bottom and edges are golden browns (20 to 40 minutes). Remove from the oven and let cool. Complete with the rocket and mayonnaise.

5) Potato and cauliflower meatballs with yogurt sauce

Ingredients:
- 300 ml of soy yogurt
- 250 g of cauliflower
- 450 g of potatoes
- 150 g of chickpea flour
- 1 tablespoon of chopped fresh parsley
- 1 teaspoon of turmeric
- 1 teaspoon of thyme
- oil
- salt and pepper

Clean the cauliflower, divide it into florets and wash it. Peel the potatoes, rinse them, and cut them into squares. Steam the two ingredients for about 15 minutes or boil them in boiling water. While they are cooking, mix the yogurt with a pinch of salt and parsley. Set it aside. Let the vegetables cool and mash them with a potato masher, collecting the past in a bowl. Add the chickpea flour, thyme, turmeric, salt, and pepper. Stir with the spoon. When the mixture is homogeneous (if it were too soft, add more chickpea flour), take small portions with wet hands and make spherical balls with a diameter of about 4 cm. Arrange them in a pan brushed with oil. Bake at 180 degrees for 15 minutes, turning them a couple of times. Serve hot, accompanied with the yogurt sauce.

6) Mashed fava beans

Ingredients:

- **250 g of broad beans**

- **1 white onion**

- **4 tablespoons of oil**

- **2 cloves of garlic**

- **salt**

Rinse the previously soaked broad beans overnight and boil them with the garlic for about 2 hours in a saucepan. Peel and chop the onion; put them in a large pan with a tablespoon of oil and a glass of water. Salt and cook over medium heat, uncovered, for about 10 minutes, until the liquid is used up. At the end, turn off and season with a little oil. Blend the beans and onion by immersion, season with the salt and the remaining oil; serve as a side dish.

7) Broccoli and tofu meatballs

Ingredients:
- **1 large or 2 small broccoli**
- **200 g of tofu**
- **1 tablespoon of barley miso**
- **1 tablespoon of oil**
- **breadcrumbs (if necessary)**
- **Sesame seeds**
- **salad of your choice**

Clean and wash the broccoli, including the stem (remove the hardest part). Steam it for a few minutes, just long enough to soften it, then chop it in a blender with the tofu, the miso dissolved in a little water from the vegetable and the oil; if the mixture is too soft, add some breadcrumbs a little at a time. Shape into balls 3-4 cm in diameter and pass them in the sesame seeds. Place them on a baking sheet lined with parchment paper and place them in a ventilated oven for 20 minutes at 180 °. Serve on a bed of shredded salad leaves.

8) Baked zucchini with curry

Ingredients:
- **5 zucchini**
- **4 tablespoons of pumpkin seeds**
- **1 tablespoon of chia seeds**
- **1 teaspoon of curry powder**
- **lemon juice**
- **black pepper**
- **extra virgin olive oil**
- **sea salt**

Wash the zucchini well and cut them into 4 lengthwise. Put them in a baking dish, sprinkle with oil, salt and bake at 180 °. Cook for about 25 minutes, turning them often. Let the vegetables cool slightly. Season with lemon juice, more oil if necessary, season with salt, pepper and complete with pumpkin and chia seeds, which you will distribute on the surface with the curry. Serve immediately.

9)   Avocado flans

Ingredients:
- **2 small avocados**
- **300 ml of soy milk**
- **50 grams of almond flour**
- **100 grams of tofu**
- **1 teaspoon of marjoram**
- **2 tablespoons of breadcrumbs**
- **2 tablespoons of sesame**
- **salt and pepper as required**
- **3 tablespoons of extra virgin olive oil**

Heat the milk almost to the boil and add salt. Toast the flour over low heat in a small saucepan. Pass it through a sieve and put it back in the container. Slowly add the hot milk, always stirring to prevent lumps from forming. Return the saucepan to heat and cook the sauce over low heat, stirring it, until it thickens. Top with chili and creamy tofu. To obtain the tofu cream, blanch the dough in a saucepan with hot water and a pinch of salt for a few minutes, then drain the well and mash it vigorously with the pressure of a fork. Grease 4 single-portion molds with a little oil. Peel the avocados and pit them. Mash the pulp with a knife and mix it with the prepared sauce. Mix everything well and taste salt. Spread the mixture into molds, sprinkle the surface with little breadcrumbs mixed with sesame seeds and marjoram. Bake at 180 degrees for about 20 minutes. Serve the flans hot or warm accompanied by a fresh seasonal salad enriched with walnuts and pine nuts and dressed with oil, salt and soy sauce, and a few slices of wholemeal bread.

10) Millet pizza

Ingredients:
- 250 g of millet flour
- 250 g of rice flour
- 100 g of chickpea flour
- 300 ml of tomato sauce
- 4 eggs
- 15 boiled green beans
- 1 tablespoon of oregano
- salt
- oil
- ½ cube of brewer's yeast
- 400 ml of water

Put the three types of flour and the water you have dissolved the brewer's yeast in a bowl. Work the mixture well and let it rise in a warm place, covered with a cloth, for 6-7 hours. Knead again by adding 1 tablespoon of salt and spread to a thickness of 2 cm on a baking sheet lined with baking paper. Let rise for 1-2 hours, then bake in a preheated oven at 180-190 ° for 35-40 minutes. After this time, sprinkle the pasta base with the tomato sauce, leaving the edges free. Break the eggs on top and cook for another 10 minutes. Finally, season the green beans with salt and oil and distribute them on the pizza, sprinkling everything with oregano.

11) Buckwheat snack with chilli and sesame

Ingredients:
- **200 g of buckwheat flour**
- **200 g of wholemeal flour**
- **80 ml of oil**
- **140 ml of white wine**
- **1 tablespoon of cream of tartar**
- **1 tablespoon of salt**
- **1 tablespoon of chilli powder**
- **4 tablespoons of sesame**

Mix the flours with oil, salt, cream of tartar, wine, chili, and 3 tablespoons of sesame. Work the ingredients until the mixture is soft and smooth. Form a ball and let it rest for about 30 minutes. Take the dough and roll it out very thin on a pastry board. Make many discs using a glass or a pastry cutter. Place them on a baking sheet lined with parchment paper that you have just greased with oil. Prick them with a fork, brush them with oil and sprinkle with the remaining sesame. Cook them for about 15 minutes at 180 °. This snack is great for a snack or as an accompaniment to a sauce.

12) Glasses of roasted pumpkin and tofu cream

Ingredients:
- **500 g of pumpkin already cleaned**
- **150 g of tofu**
- **4 tablespoons of oil**
- **4 tablespoons of broth**
- **2 teaspoons of white miso**
- **1 clove of garlic**
- **2 bay leaves**
- **salt**
- **pepper**

For the hazelnut granola
- **4 spoonfuls of oat flakes**
- **4 heaping tablespoons of toasted and chopped hazelnuts**
- **2 tablespoons of oil**
- **1 tablespoon of rice malt**
- **1 pinch of mixed five-spice pleasure**

Cut the pumpkin into cubes and season with 3 tablespoons of oil, the crushed garlic, salt, pepper, and bay leaf. Bake it in a covered pan for about 20 minutes at 180 degrees, until tender. Blanch the tofu for 5 minutes in water, taking care to let it simmer to prevent it from becoming spongy. When it has cooled, drain it with a tablespoon of oil, the broth, and the miso, until you get a creamy consistency. Mix the remaining ingredients in a bowl and distribute them in a baking dish; cook in the oven at 180 ° for 15-20 minutes, occasionally stirring, until golden brown. Let it cool down.

Chapter 6: Soups and Salads

1) Radicchio and pear salad with ginger

Ingredients:
- 2 head of radicchio
- 2 pears
- 4 walnuts
- 4 sprigs of parsley
- vinegar to taste
- 1 piece of ginger
- 3 tablespoons of oil

Peel and wash the radicchio, then dry them with the centrifuge and cut them into strips not too thin. Gather them in a salad bowl. Add the chopped walnuts, the chopped parsley. Peel the pears and cut them into cubes. Mix them with the radicchio. Season with salt, vinegar, and oil. Peel and grate the ginger. Squeeze it very well in a cloth to extract all the juice, which you will pour on the vegetables. Stir and serve.

2) Cream of fennel and leeks

Ingredients:
- 300 g of clean fennel
- 300 g of leeks
- ½ teaspoon of chopped fennel seeds
- 4 teaspoons of toasted sunflower seeds
- salt

Wash the fennel and leeks well; of the latter, also use the green part. Finely slice the first courses, halve the second courses for a long time, and then cut them into slices or strips. Bring 800 ml of salted water to a boil and toss in the leeks. Blanch them for a minute, then add the fennel and fennel seeds, cover and cook gently for 15 minutes. Blend, put back on the heat, and simmer for a few minutes. Serve by distributing the sunflower seeds on the surface.

3) Curry rice and cabbage soup

Ingredients:
- 600 g of white cabbage
- 150 g of brown rice
- 2 tablespoons of extra virgin olive oil
- 1 teaspoon of turmeric powder
- 1 teaspoon of spicy curry
- 1 teaspoon of vegetable cube powder
- salt
- pepper

Wash the rice and place it in a saucepan with 300 ml of water; when it boils, add 2 pinches of salt. Cover and cook on low heat until the water has been completely absorbed. Clean the vegetables and cut them into florets. Bring a liter of water to a boil and add the green broccoli for 5 minutes, keeping its bright color (the water is already hot for this). Then remove it with a slotted spoon and keep it aside. Also, keep the liquid, which will be used for the soup. Heat the oil in a saucepan, add the white cabbage, the vegetable cube, the turmeric, and the curry. Leave to flavor for a minute, continuing to stir. Pour the set aside water and bring back to a boil, add salt and cook for 15 minutes. Add the rice and continue cooking for another 5 minutes. Complete with the green broccoli, which will give a touch of color, taste and serve with a sprinkling of pepper.

4) Chickpeas with summer vegetables

Ingredients:
- **250 g of dried chickpeas**
- **8-10 cherry tomatoes**
- **1 medium cucumber**
- **½ red onion**
- **1 handful of capers**
- **1 small handful of fresh basil**
- **3-4 large handfuls of fresh parsley**
- **the juice of 1 lemon**
- **oil, to taste**
- **chilli powder**
- **sea salt to taste**

Soak the chickpeas in filtered water for 8-10 hours, rinse them under running water, and cook them in water with a sea salt pinch. In the meantime, take the salted capers, soak them in water for 10-15 minutes and then rinse them, squeeze them well and chop them. When the chickpeas are cooked, remove them from the heat, pass them under cold running water and transfer them to a salad bowl to let them cool. As soon as the chickpeas are cold, add the cleaned and sliced tomatoes to the salad bowl, the cleaned cucumber and cut into thin slices, the capers, parsley, and basil, washed and chopped, the peeled and thinly sliced onion, the juice of the lemon and chili. Season with oil and salt, mix everything well, and refrigerate for at least 20 minutes. The dish should be served cold.

5) Velvety Asparagus

Ingredients:
- 500 g of white asparagus
- 500 g of green asparagus
- 500 g of white potatoes
- 2 fresh white spring onions
- 700 ml of vegetable broth
- 1 tablespoon of vegetable butter
- 3 tablespoons of vegetable cream

to garnish
- salt
- pink pepper
- fresh mint

For this cream, the asparagus must be as fresh as possible. Separate the hardest part of the asparagus, peel it and cut it into thin slices together with the tips. Put everything in a bowl full of water. Peel the potatoes and divide them into small cubes. Clean the spring onions and slice them finely, then brown them for a few minutes in a saucepan where you have melted the butter over low heat, being careful not to burn them. Add the vegetables, cook, and sprinkle with the vegetable broth. Bring to a boil, add salt and cook for 30 minutes over low heat until the vegetables are soft. To make sure they don't leave strands, you can purée them for the first time with the classic vegetable mill. If the result satisfies you, leave everything as it is, otherwise blends the immersion cream again to make it creamier. Complete with the vegetable cream, serve in bowls, and garnish with a little cream, minced mint, and pink pepper sprinkling.

6) Vegetable soup with garlic toast

Ingredients:
- 300 g of cooked beans
- 300 g of cabbage leaves
- 300 g of small carrots
- 200 g of white onion
- 200 g of celery
- 200 g of leek
- 50 g of baby spinach
- 2 tablespoons of tomato puree
- bread (gluten free if intolerant to gluten)
- garlic
- 4 tablespoons of oil
- extra virgin olive oil
- 1 tablespoon of vegetable cube
- 1 bunch of herbs (rosemary, bay leaf, thyme, sage)
- salt

Carefully peel and wash all the vegetables. Cut the carrots into slices; slice the leek and onion; reduce the celery into not too small cubes. Separate the cabbage's central rib and cut it into small pieces; divide the leaves into strips and then into squares. Tie the bunch of herbs with the kitchen string after having cleaned it well. Heat 2 tablespoons of oil in a saucepan and let it flavor, stirring for a few minutes, the vegetables prepared with the bunch of herbs, the vegetable cube, and the tomato puree. At this point, add just over a liter of water and the beans. Bring to a boil, lightly salt, and cook over low heat for 30 minutes, a few minutes before the end of cooking, complete with the baby spinach. Meanwhile, cut the bread into slices, then toast it for 10 minutes in the oven brought to 160 °. Serve the hot soup in bowls, accompanied by croutons rubbed with a clove of garlic and drizzled with the rest of the oil.

7) Waldorf salad

Ingredients:
- **200 g of clean celeriac**
- **200 g of apples**
- **50 g of walnut kernels**
- **50 g of rocket**
- **100 g of mayonnaise**
- **the juice of 1 lemon + 2 tablespoons of juice**
- **2 tablespoons of plain yogurt**
- **pepper**
- **salt**

Cut the celeriac into strips about 5 cm long and half a centimeter thick. Cook it in salted water for 1-2 minutes, drain it and throw it in cold water and ice. Then dry it well with a cloth. Now prepare the sauce. Pour the mayonnaise into a bowl and mix it well with the yogurt, two tablespoons of lemon juice, a sprinkle of pepper, and a little salt. Core the apple, peel it, and cut it in the same way as the celeriac. Put it in water with the lemon juice, then drain it. Now gather the prepared ingredients and the coarsely chopped walnuts in a bowl. Mix everything well and place a bed of rockets on the plates.

8)   Mushroom soup with celeriac meatballs

Ingredients:
- 120 g of fresh mushrooms
- 200 g of leek
- 200 g of carrots
- 1 tablespoon of vegetable butter

For the broth
- 1 clean celery stick
- 5 slices of dried mushrooms
- 4 cloves
- salt

For the meatballs
- 500 g of celeriac
- 100 g of bread (gluten free if intolerant)
4 tablespoons of cooked beans
- 1 tablespoon of parsley
- 2 tablespoons of breadcrumbs (gluten free if intolerant)
- 1 teaspoon of ginger juice
- salt

For the broth: Put the celery in a pot with a liter of lightly salted water and the other ingredients; cook for 15 minutes and strain. For the meatballs: Peel the celeriac with a potato peeler, wash it and slice it finely. Steam it for about 15 minutes until soft. Put the bread in a bowl, preferably without a crust, soften it with a little hot broth and squeeze it. Then gather the cooked celeriac, the soaked bread, the beans, the ginger juice, the salt, and the chopped parsley in the mixer. Work them until they are amalgamated, then remove the mixture from the mixer and add the breadcrumbs. Divide it into many similar size pieces, to which you will give a round or oval shape; let it rest. Clean the leek well, pass the fresh porcini mushrooms with a damp cloth to remove the earth; cut the first into slices and the second into cubes.

Peel the carrots and cut them into medium-small cubes. Melt the butter and brown the vegetables for a few minutes, then add the rest of the broth. Cook in 20 minutes. Add the meatballs to the soup, which you will serve hot on plates.

9) Coleslaw

Ingredients:
- ¼ of white cabbage
- 2 carrots
- 1 pinch of salt
- 1 lemon

for the sauce:
- 100 g of tofu
- ½ tablespoon of miso
- 1 tablespoon of lemon juice
- 1-2 tablespoons of lightly toasted sesame or sunflower seeds
- 1 spring onion

Cut the cabbage into very thin threads and mix them with the salt, pressing well with your hands; let it rest under pressure for at least an hour. Grate the carrots and sprinkle them with lemon juice. Blanch the tofu in water for 5 minutes (taking care not to boil it too vigorously because it acquires a stringy consistency); then blend it, mixing well with the sauce's remaining ingredients. Squeeze the cabbage, mix with carrots, and season with the sauce.

10) Spiced lentil and pumpkin soup

Ingredients:
- 300 g of dried lentils
- 1 bay leaf
- 800 g of pumpkin
- 2 shallots
- 20 g of hazelnuts
- 900 ml of vegetable broth
- 2 teaspoons of extra virgin olive oil
- ½ teaspoon of cardamom powder
- ½ teaspoon of coriander
- 1 sprig of thyme
- salt

Soak the lentils for 6-8 hours, checking that they do not contain impurities. Drain and boil them in a liter of water with the bay leaf for about 30 minutes. Salt only at the end. Toast the cardamom and coriander in a thick-bottomed saucepan, stirring, until you can smell their scent. Add the oil, stir and add the peeled and chopped shallots and the peeled pumpkin, seeded, and cut into not too small cubes. Stir for a few seconds with a wooden spoon to flavor and pour in the vegetable broth. Bring to a boil, lightly salt, and cook for about 20 minutes. Take half of the pumpkin and reduce it in the mixer into a homogeneous puree. Put it back in the soup with the drained lentils and boil for a few more minutes, taste, and possibly add salt. Put the hazelnuts in the oven for 10-15 minutes at 150 °; when they are warm, you will need to be able to remove the skin by rubbing them between your fingers. Chop them and use them to garnish the soup served hot in the bowls, sprinkled with peeled thyme.

11) Corn soup with black cabbage and beans

Ingredients:
- 150 g of dried beans
- 70 g of celery
- 80 g of carrots
- 40 g of leek
- 80 g of black cabbage
- 1 clove of garlic
- 50 g of corn flour
- 1.2 l of water or vegetable broth
- 2 tablespoons of oil
- extra virgin olive oil
- 2 bay leaves
- fresh or powdered chili
- salt

Soak the beans for at least 12 hours. Change the water several times, drain and cook them in plenty of fresh water with 2 bay leaves for an hour and a half. In the meantime, clean and wash the vegetables well. Cut the leek and carrots into rounds, the ribs, and celery leaves into small pieces; peel the garlic and halve it. Gather all the vegetables in the mixer and operate until the mixture is not too fine. Separate the black cabbage leaves from the stem and chop them with a knife. In a saucepan with high sides, heat the oil, transfer all the vegetables to it, cook them over medium heat for a few minutes, and stir. Pour in the water or broth and add salt; bring to a boil and pour in the flour, stirring. Continue cooking for 40 minutes, over low heat, and with the lid slightly shifted. In the end, season with chopped fresh chili pepper or a sprinkling of the powder. Add the beans and mix carefully. Serve the soup very hot.

12) Cream of chestnuts

Ingredients:
- 400 g of dried chestnuts
- 400 ml of oat milk
- 30 g of walnuts
- 4 tablespoons of yogurt
- nutmeg
- parsley
- salt

Soak the dried chestnuts for 8 hours. After this time, cook them in the pressure cooker with 600 ml of water for 30 minutes. Using another cooking pan, it will take an hour on low heat. Then add the oat milk, salt lightly, and work with the hand blender until you get a more or less homogeneous puree according to your preferences. Serve hot in bowls and garnish each portion with a tablespoon of yogurt, a light mixture of lightly toasted walnuts, a few finely chopped parsley leaves, and a sprinkling of nutmeg.

Chapter 7: Fish

1) Mackerel in foil

Ingredients:
- Mackerel (2 clean mackerel)
- Celery 90 g
- Yellow peppers 70 g
- Tomatoes 60 g
- Eggplant 50 g
- Lemons 1
- Basil to taste
- Extra virgin olive oil q.s.
- Black pepper to taste
- Salt up to taste

Chop the celery and cut it into cubes, then cut the eggplants into slices and cut into cubes. Remove the internal seeds and the stalk of the pepper and cut it first into strips and then into cubes. Finally, cut the tomatoes into cubes. Transfer all the cut vegetables to a bowl, scented with fresh basil leaves and season with oil, salt and pepper. Now place each clean mackerel on a 35x31 cm sheet of parchment paper, fill the belly of the mackerel with a spoonful of vegetables and then distribute the rest around the fish. Season the fish with a drizzle of olive oil. Wash the lemon and cut into thin slices, then place 3 lemon slices on top of each mackerel. Now close the parcel by lifting the flaps of parchment paper and placing them on top of the fish, then seal well by folding the sides. Place the packets on a baking tray lined with parchment paper and bake in a preheated static oven at 200 ° for 20 minutes. When cooked, take your mackerel in foil out of the oven and serve hot.

2) Orange mackerel

Ingredients:
- Mackerel (4 whole clean) 1200 g
- Orange peel 1
- Extra virgin olive oil q.s.

FOR MARINATING
- Orange juice
- Extra virgin olive oil 30 g
- Dill 2 sprigs
- 2 cloves garlic
- Black peppercorns 1 tbsp
- Salt up to 1 tbsp

Make diagonal cuts on the sides of the mackerel and set aside. Take care of the ingredients for the marinade: with the back of the spoon, crush the peppercorns so they will release their aroma better, then squeeze the juice from the oranges. Peel and thinly slice the garlic. Grease a baking dish with oil, place the mackerel on top and season them on the surface with another drizzle of oil, the peppercorns, salt, scented with the sprigs of dill and flavored with the slices of garlic. Finally, sprinkle the fish with half of the orange juice, cover with plastic wrap and leave to marinate for 2 hours in the refrigerator. After the marinating time, go to cooking: heat a pan with a drizzle of olive oil and, when it is hot, lay the fillets. Let them cook over high heat for 4 minutes without touching them, then turn them, sprinkle them with the remaining orange juice and continue cooking for another 2 minutes. Once the sauce has congealed and the mackerel are well flavored, serve them immediately garnishing them with grated orange zest on the surface.

3) Spaghetti with anchovies and breadcrumbs

Ingredients:
- **Spaghetti 320 g**
- **Anchovies in oil 30 g**
- **Extra virgin olive oil 20 g**
- **Breadcrumbs 70 g**
- **3 cloves garlic**

Put a pan with water on the heat and bring to a boil: it will then be used to cook the pasta. Meanwhile, pour 10 g of extra virgin olive oil into a pan, then add the peeled garlic cloves and the anchovy fillets drained from the preservation oil. Peel a ladle of hot water and pour it into the pan, so you can melt the anchovies in the best possible way. This will take about 10 minutes so stir often. Meanwhile, in a separate pan pour 10 g of extra virgin olive oil, then add breadcrumbs to toast it and mix everything until the crumbs are golden; keep aside. At this point, cook the pasta in boiling water; you can add at most very little coarse salt if you prefer, as anchovies are very tasty. Cook the spaghetti for the time indicated on the package. After the time has elapsed, remove the garlic cloves from the saucepan and drain the pasta by dipping it directly into the pan. Add some of the breadcrumbs and mix. If necessary, add a little more cooking water, then serve your spaghetti with the anchovies and garnish with a final sprinkling of breadcrumbs.

4)   Baked sardines

Ingredients:
- **18 sardines for a total of about 250 g**
- **Breadcrumbs 60 g**
- **Extra virgin olive oil 60 g**
- **1 sprig parsley**
- **Thyme 1 sprig**
- **1 clove garlic**
- **Grated Parmesan cheese 20 g**
- **Pine nuts 30 g**
- **Extra virgin olive oil to grease the pan 15g**

Pour the breadcrumbs, grated cheese and the crushed garlic clove into a bowl. Rinse, dry and finely chop the parsley; then also add it to the breading and further flavor with the thyme leaves; pour the 60 g of oil and mix everything until you get a uniform mixture. At this point take a baking dish measuring 19x15 cm and sprinkle it with about 15 g of oil. Arrange the sardines horizontally without overlapping each other, salt (not excessively), pepper and cover with half of the previously prepared mixture. Arrange another layer of sardines, taking care to position them vertically (opposite to before), salt, pepper and cover the entire surface with the remaining part of the breading. Finish by decorating the surface with pine nuts. Then cook the sardines in the oven in grill mode at 200 ° for 8 minutes, until they are golden brown. Once cooked, serve the baked sardines while still hot.

5) Tuna glazed with soy sauce

Ingredients:
- Tuna fillet 400 g
- Red cabbage 500 g
- Soy sauce 50 g
- White wine vinegar 100 g
- Salt up to 30 g
- Extra virgin olive oil 20 g
- Basil 4 leaves
- Sesame seeds 30 g

Start with the vegetables: julienne the cabbage and place it in a bowl, sprinkling with white wine vinegar and seasoning with salt. Mix the ingredients well and leave to macerate for at least 1 hour, covering with cling film. After this time, drain and rinse the cabbage thoroughly under plenty of running water. Then cook it in a non-stick pan in which you have heated 15 g of oil. Flavored with well washed and dried basil leaves and cover with a lid, cooking over low heat for about 10 minutes. When cooked, the cabbage should still be crunchy. While the cabbage is cooking, dedicate yourself to the tuna. Take a small bowl and pour the soy sauce. Take care of the tuna: make sure you have a fillet already cut down; we advise you to freeze the fillet for at least 96 hours at -18 degrees and then defrost for preparation. Cut the tuna into slices about 4 cm thick. Then place a small bowl next to the soy sauce in which you will have poured the white sesame seeds. Take a slice of tuna and wet it on all sides with the soy sauce, then completely cover the long sides of the tuna slice with sesame seeds. Repeat the operation with all the slices of tuna. Now take a non-stick pan and pour in 5 g of oil: heat it up and place the slices of tuna on the long sides. Blanch the tuna slices for about 2 minutes, then flip them to cook them on the other side for another 2 minutes. For even cooking, you can also sear the tuna slices sideways, 1 minute on each side. Place a bed of cabbage on the serving dish and arrange the slices of tuna on top of it, accompanying with the soy sauce.

Your tuna glazed with soy sauce is then ready to be brought to the table and enjoyed!

6) Spaghetti with tuna

Ingredients:
- Spaghetti 320 g
- Tuna in oil (drained) 150 g
- Peeled tomatoes 400 g
- Extra virgin olive oil q.s.
- Salt up to taste
- Black pepper to taste
- Basil to taste
- Onions ½

Start by putting a pot full of water on the stove, add salt to taste when boiling: it will be used for cooking the pasta. Drain the tuna fillet from the conservation oil. Meanwhile, peel the onion, slice it thinly. Heat the olive oil in a pan and add the sliced onion. Let it dry over low heat for a few minutes, stirring often; fray the tuna with your hands and add it to the pan when the onion is soft and let it brown for a couple of minutes, stirring constantly. Now, mash the tomatoes with a fork and pour them into the pan with the tuna; let the sauce cook for about 10 minutes. Meanwhile, cook the spaghetti, while the pasta is cooking, the sauce will also be ready. Drain the spaghetti directly into the pan with the tuna, season with the ground pepper, turn off the heat and perfume with the fresh basil leaves. Stir and serve your tuna spaghetti hot!

7) Tuna tartare

Ingredients:
- **Tuna in slices 450 g**
- **Oranges 1**
- **Extra virgin olive oil 40 g**
- **Salt up to taste**
- **Black pepper to taste**
- **Shortcrust pastry 230 g**
- **Wild fennel 3 sprigs**

Start grating the zest of an orange, then cut it in half and squeeze the juice. In a bowl, pour the extra virgin olive oil, the orange juice and its zest. Finely chop the fennel, keeping a few strands aside for the final decoration, add it to the mixture and emulsify with a whisk. Meanwhile, prepare the shortcrust pastry shells. Adjust the emulsion with a pinch of pepper and salt. Prepare the shortcrust pastry shells that will be used to make tartare single portions: roll out the shortcrust pastry (you can use a roll of already made shortcrust pastry), cut out 10 circles of about 10 cm in diameter and line 10 round molds with a diameter of 8 cm , after having buttered them. Prick the bottom with the tines of a fork and cook in white, covered with dried legumes as weight, in the oven at 180 degrees for 10-15 minutes. When they are golden, take them out of the oven, let them cool and turn them out. Take the tuna steaks: make sure you have bought especially fish. It is recommended to freeze it for 96 hours at -18 degrees and then defrost it for use in the recipe. Rinse and dry the tuna fillets with absorbent paper. Cut them into small cubes half a centimeter thick and place them in a large bowl. Pour the oil and orange emulsion over them and mix so that the tuna is well flavored. Then fill the cakes with one or two tablespoons of tuna tartare and decorate your tartare with a few sprigs of fennel.

8) Tuna in pistachio crust

Ingredients:
- Tuna 600 g
- Poppy seeds 1 tbsp
- Extra virgin olive oil 3 tbsp
- Breadcrumbs 20 g
- Chopped pistachios 50
- Dried tomatoes in oil 30 g
- Salt up to taste

Get yourself a slice of fresh tuna, place the slice in the freezer for at least an hour so that it is more convenient to cut without breaking the fibers. Remove the tuna from the freezer and cut it lengthwise into slices about 2-3 cm thick. Put the tuna slices in a baking dish and drizzle them with the olive oil. Meanwhile, dry the dried tomatoes with a cloth to remove excess oil and chop finely with a knife. Place the chopped pistachios in a bowl, add the chopped tomatoes, poppy seeds and breadcrumbs. Stir to mix the ingredients well and salt the breading to taste. Take the slices of tuna and pass them in the breadcrumbs, pressing well on all sides. Place a couple of tablespoons of extra virgin olive oil in a non-stick pan and once the necessary heat is reached, add the breaded tuna slices and cook them for 1 minute per side, turning them only once. Do not continue cooking so that the tuna remains pink inside, the tuna must not turn white otherwise the meat will be harder. Remove the pistachio crusted tuna from the pan and cut into 2 cm thick slices, then place them on a serving dish and serve immediately.

9) Mediterranean-style salmon fillets

Ingredients:
- Salmon 800 g
- Cherry tomatoes 350 g
- Dried oregano 1 sprig
- Extra virgin olive oil 30 g
- Salt up to taste
- 1 clove garlic
- Pitted black olives 70 g
- Pickled capers 5 g

Start washing the tomatoes, then dry them and cut them into 4. Transfer them to a large bowl, add the peeled and halved garlic and the chopped dried oregano. Add the oil, salt, mix everything and cover with cling film. Let the tomatoes macerate for about 1 hour at room temperature. After this time, take the salmon steak and remove any bones with tweezers and remove the skin if it is present; then cut into 4 fillets of equal thickness. Take back the cherry tomatoes, remove the garlic and transfer them to a lightly greased baking dish. Arrange the salmon fillets on top of the cherry tomatoes and with a teaspoon take some cherry tomatoes and arrange them on top of the salmon. Salt, pepper, add the black olives and capers. Bake in a preheated static oven at 180 ° for about 15 minutes (if you want to use the convection oven, bake at 160 ° for about 10 minutes). After this time, take out and serve your Mediterranean salmon fillets still hot!

10) Salmon rice

Ingredients:
- Rice 350 g
- Salmon steaks 250 g
- Leeks 1
- Extra virgin olive oil q.s.
- 1 clove garlic
- ½ glass white wine
- Parmesan to be grated 20 g
- Salt up to taste
- Black pepper to taste
- Fish broth 500 ml

FOR THE FLAVORED BUTTER
- Butter 80 g
- Marjoram 1 sprig
- Dill 1 sprig
- Thyme 1 sprig
- Lemon zest ½
- Salt up to taste

Prepare the flavored butter by chopping the herbs and grating the lemon zest, allow the butter to soften at room temperature and when it has reached a creamy consistency add the chopped herbs, lemon zest and salt. Meanwhile, clean the salmon steak and cut it into small pieces. Heat a tablespoon of oil in a pan with a clove of whole garlic and brown the salmon bites for 2/3 minutes, add salt and set the salmon aside, removing the garlic. Now start preparing the risotto: finely chop the leek and sauté it over low heat with two tablespoons of oil in a pan. Pour in the rice and toast it for a few moments over high heat, stirring with a wooden spoon. Deglaze with the counter wine and continue cooking, stirring occasionally, taking care that the rice does not stick, adding the broth (vegetable or fish) a little at a time.

Halfway through cooking add the salmon morsels, season with salt if necessary and when the rice is well cooked, remove it from the heat and stir in the herb-flavored butter and a couple of tablespoons of grated cheese, if you like.

11) Baked salmon

Ingredients:
- **Salmon steaks (4 pieces) 660 g**
- **Potatoes 170 g**
- **Lemon zest 1**
- **Lemon juice 25 g**
- **Dry white wine 25 g**
- **Extra virgin olive oil 50 g**
- **Parsley to chop 1 tbsp**
- **Salt up to taste**
- **Black pepper to taste**

To prepare the baked salmon, first remove the fish bones with tweezers and check that there are no bones left by sliding a fingertip on the pulp. Remove the spine with a knife, then roll one end on itself and wrap the other end around the slice to obtain a medallion. Tie the medallion with a kitchen string to ensure that it maintains the shape even during cooking and transfer the medallions on a baking sheet lined with parchment paper. Take a fairly regular shaped potato, wash it and cut it into thin slices with a mandolin, without peeling it: the slices must be no more than 1 mm thick otherwise they will not be cooked enough. Now take care of the emulsion: grate the zest of a lemon in a bowl, then add 25 g of lemon juice, oil, white wine, chopped parsley, salt and pepper and mix well with a fork. Season the salmon medallions with part of the emulsion, then cover them with the slightly overlapping potato discs and sprinkle the potatoes with the remaining emulsion. When the medallions are ready, bake in a preheated static oven at 180 ° for about 20 minutes, then operate the grill at 240 ° and continue cooking for another 3-4 minutes, until the potatoes are golden.

After the cooking time has elapsed, remove the cooking string and immediately serve your delicious baked salmon!

12) Crispy salmon

Ingredients:
- Salmon fillet (4 of 250 g each) 1 kg
- Bread 100 g
- 1 sprig parsley
- Dill 1 sprig
- Thyme 4 sprigs
- Rosemary 2 sprigs
- Lemon zest 1
- Extra virgin olive oil 50 g
- White pepper in grains 1 tsp
- Salt up to taste

First, prepare the breading: cut the bread into pieces and put it in a mixer, then add the dill, the peeled thyme, the needles of rosemary and parsley. Pour in the oil too, then add the lemon zest, salt and white pepper. Blend until you get a coarse consistency. Now take care of the salmon fillets: remove the skin with a thin-bladed knife and remove the bones with the help of a kitchen tongs, then transfer the fillets to a drip pan lined with parchment paper and cover them with the breading, making it adhere well with your hands. . After covering the fillets evenly, cook in a preheated convection oven at 190 ° for about 20 minutes. After the cooking time, take out and serve your crispy salmon hot!

Chapter 8: Meat

1) Salad baskets with turkey

Ingredients:
- **Turkey breast 250 g**
- **Baby lettuce 100 g**
- **Cashews 25 g**
- **Carrots 1**
- **Parsley to taste**
- **Extra virgin olive oil q.s.**

Place the turkey breast on a cutting board and cut it into irregular pieces. Then take a non-stick pan, heat a drizzle of oil. Add the turkey breast bites and salt. Cook the morsels for about 10 minutes, turning them from time to time to cook them inside until they are golden brown. When the turkey morsels are cooked, transfer them to a mixer, operate for a few seconds until the meat is well chopped, and then transfer the blended mixture into a large bowl. At this point, place the cashews on a cutting board and chop them coarsely. Sauté the chopped cashews in a non-stick pan and toast them for a few minutes, until crisp and darker. Then add the toasted cashews to the chopped turkey bites. Then take a carrot, peel it and divide it in half. After that, slice it into tiny cubes. Also, wash the parsley under running water and chop finely on a cutting board. At this point, add the diced carrot and chopped parsley to the mixture. Now wash the salad carefully and leaf it through, placing the crispest and most curved leaves on a serving dish. Then proceed to fill them with the dough. Your baskets of lettuce with turkey are ready to be served.

2) Meatballs in sesame crust

Ingredients:
- **Minced veal 300 g**
- **Wholemeal bread crumb 65 g**
- **Parmesan (for grating) 50 g**
- **Sesame seeds 50 g**
- **Black sesame seeds 25 g**
- **Eggs 1**
- **Salt up to taste**

Cut the wholemeal bread crumb into cubes, removing the outer crust, and crumble it in a mixer. In a large bowl, pour the veal, mixing them with your hands; add the chopped breadcrumbs, then the grated cheese. Incorporate the egg and season with salt. Mix with your hands until you get a homogeneous mixture. Each and continue like this until you finish the mix available: with our doses, you will have to obtain 38 meatballs. Pour the white sesame seeds into a tray and add them to the black sesame seeds, mixing them carefully. Pass the meatballs over the sesame, making it stick well to the meat. Continue in this way with all the remaining meatballs and, once finished, arrange them side by side on a baking tray lined with baking paper. Bake the meatballs in a preheated static oven at 180 ° for about 25 minutes, seasoning them with a drizzle of oil if necessary. After the required time, take out of the oven and enjoy your sesame-crusted meatballs hot.

3) Veal slices with mushrooms

Ingredients:
- **Veal (walnut) 400 g**
- **Champignon mushrooms 500 g**
- **Vegetable butter 50 g**
- **00 flour 40 g**
- **Extra virgin olive oil 10 g**
- **Salt up to taste**
- **Thyme to taste**
- **1 sprig chopped rosemary**

Take the veal slices, and with the meat mallet, slice them to make them thinner, flour the veal slices on both sides, and then shake them to remove the excess flour. Now take care of cleaning the mushrooms: with a small knife, begin to remove the earthy part on the stem, scraping it gently until any traces of earth are removed. If the mushroom is clean enough, remove the few earth residues with a brush, do not wash them with water to not spoil them. Slice the mushrooms and set them aside. Now proceed with cooking the meat: In a pan, melt half a dose of butter (25 g), adding the olive oil; once melted, lay the floured veal slices, add salt and brown them for 3 minutes per side or until a crust forms. Once golden brown, let them cool on a plate and take care of the mushrooms: In the same pan in which you cooked the meat, melt the other half of the butter, season with the chopped rosemary, add the sliced mushrooms and sauté over medium heat for two minutes. , then add salt. At this point, add the veal slices browned and kept aside and flavored with the thyme leaves, cook over low heat for a minute, adding a ladle of water if necessary, and serve the veal with the mushrooms very hot!

4) Tasty chicken wings and potatoes

Ingredients:
- Chicken wings 8
- Potatoes 500 g
- Breadcrumbs 200 g
- 00 flour 50 g
- Parmesan to grate 50 g
- Eggs 2
- Parsley to be minced to taste
- Extra virgin olive oil as needed
- Salt up to taste

First, pour the flour into a bowl and flour the chicken wings on both sides, remove the excess flour and place them on a tray. In another bowl, pour the breadcrumbs, grated Parmesan cheese, chopped parsley (keep some aside for the final garnish) and mix thoroughly. Finally, beat the eggs in another bowl again. Dip the floured chicken wings first in the beaten egg and then in the breadcrumbs and Parmesan cheese, pressing with your hands so that it adheres well. It is important to flour the meat first to prevent the breading from coming off during cooking. Once you have breaded all the chicken wings, you can take care of the potatoes. Peel the potatoes, divide them first in half and then in quarters, finally cut them into cubes. Put the potatoes in a bowl, season them with oil and salt, and then pour them into the bowl with the leftover breading and mix well. At this point, take a large pan and place the breaded chicken wings inside, then add the potatoes and distribute them evenly on the surface. Season with a little salt and a generous round of oil and cook in a preheated convection oven at 200 ° for 40 minutes. After this time, turn on the grill and continue cooking for another 10 minutes to make the breading crispy. Once cooked, garnish with the remaining parsley and serve your flavorful chicken wings and potatoes still steaming!

5) Milk chicken breasts

Ingredients:
- Sliced chicken breast 4
- Vegetable butter 40 g
- Extra virgin olive oil 10 g
- 00 flour q.s.
- Skimmed milk 170 g
- Salt up to taste
- Thyme 4 sprigs

Arrange the slices on a cutting board and, using a meat mallet, beat them to obtain thin slices. Arrange the oil and butter in a pan, let it melt gently, and in the meantime, flour the chicken slices. As you move them into the pan, raise the heat slightly and wait about 2 minutes until a nice crust has formed. Then turn the slices, wait a couple of minutes again, pour the milk first, and then the thyme leaves into the pan. Add salt, cover with a lid and let it cook for another 4-5 minutes until the milk has thickened. At this point, you just have to serve your milk-filled chicken breasts still hot!

6) Stuffed turkey rolls

Ingredients:
- **Turkey breast (4 slices)**
- **Salt up to taste**
- **Seed oil 3 tbsp**
- **Rosemary 8 sprigs**
- **Scamorza 8 slices**
- **8 slices raw ham**

Beat the slices with a meat tenderizer, wrapping them with baking paper. Take a slice of chicken and stuff it first with 2 slices of smoked cheese and then with two slices of raw ham, roll the slice on itself. Cut the roll in half that you are going to stop with a wooden skewer. Flavor each roll with a sprig of rosemary. Proceed in the same way with all the other turkey slices. Now the rolls are ready for cooking: heat a grill brushed with a little seed oil, cook the rolls on both sides, at least 6/7 minutes per side until they are well grilled, finally add salt and let them rest before serving.

7) Roasted rabbit

Ingredients:
- **Rabbit in pieces 1.2 kg**
- **Rosemary 4 sprigs**
- **Salt up to taste**
- **Vegetable broth 2000 g**
- **Potatoes 800 g**
- **Thyme 4 sprigs**
- **Bay leaf 1 leaf**
- **Extra virgin olive oil 80 g**

Chop the rosemary, then transfer half of it into a pan where you have poured 40 g of oil. Add a bay leaf and let it cook over low heat for 2-3 minutes. Raise the heat, and add the rabbit pieces; let them brown on both sides for 3-4 minutes. Add a ladle of broth and cook over low heat for another 5-6 minutes. In the meantime, prepare the potatoes: peel them and cut them into rather large chunks. Transfer everything to a bowl, flavor with the chopped rosemary needles, and set aside the thyme leaves and salt. Drizzle with 20 g of oil and mix. Transfer everything to a large pan, oiled with about 10 g of oil, so that the potatoes are well distributed. Then also arrange the previously browned rabbit pieces. Add the remaining vegetable broth and cook the rabbit with the potatoes in a preheated static oven at 200 ° for 40 minutes. Once out of the oven, serve your rabbit in the oven while still steaming!

8) Turkey chunks with saffron

Ingredients:
- Turkey breast 600 g
- Saffron (one sachet) 0.15 g
- Water about 140 g
- Extra virgin olive oil 10 g
- Potato starch 1 tsp
- 00 flour q.s.
- Salt up to taste

FOR THE ASPARAGUS
- Asparagus 400 g
- Water 100 g
- Extra virgin olive oil 10 g
- Salt up to taste

Start by cleaning the asparagus: wash them, dry them, remove the toughest end, cut them diagonally, and keep them aside. Heat the oil in a pan, add the asparagus, add salt and cook over medium heat for 7-8 minutes, adding about 100 g of water to keep the vegetables from drying out. Once they are cooked, keep them aside and take care of the turkey. Cut the turkey breast into strips and then cut them into cubes of about 1.5-2 cm. Heat a little oil in a pan. Meanwhile, flour the diced turkey in a sieve so as to remove the excess flour. Once the oil is hot, add the turkey, let it brown and then wet with about 100 g of water, or just enough to keep the turkey from drying out. Dissolve the saffron in a little warm water and add it to the preparation; add salt, stir and continue cooking; the morsels must cook in total for about 10 minutes; the time may vary according to their size. Make a cream to thicken the preparation: pour a teaspoon of starch into a small bowl, dilute it with a couple of tablespoons of water and mix to obtain a homogeneous mixture. Add the melted starch to the still hot preparation and mix. Your chicken nuggets with saffron are ready; serve them accompanied with a side of asparagus.

9) Chicken meatloaf

Ingredients:
- Minced chicken 800 g
- Swiss cheese 150 g
- Ricotta 100 g
- Parmesan to grate 50 g
- Eggs 1
- Breadcrumbs 70 g
- Marjoram 3 sprigs
- Extra virgin olive oil 10 g
- Salt up to taste

First, cut the cheese into cubes, then transfer them to a blender and blend everything. Transfer to a bowl with the minced chicken, then add the well-drained ricotta, grated cheese, marjoram leaves, salt, and egg. Knead with your hands to mix the ingredients, then add the breadcrumbs and knead again until the mixture is smooth. Pour the mixture onto a sheet of parchment paper and shape it with your hands to give it the shape of meatloaf, then wrap it in the same parchment paper and seal the roll. Leave to harden in the refrigerator for at least an hour. After this time, remove the parchment paper and heat the oil in a pan or a large pot suitable for cooking in the oven. Brown the meatloaf on all sides so that it forms a nice crust, using two stirrers or kitchen tongs to keep it from breaking. At this point, cover the pan with aluminum foil and bake at 200 ° in static mode for 60 minutes. Once cooked (if you have a thermometer, check that the internal temperature has reached 70 ° -71 °), take your chicken meatloaf out of the oven and serve it sprinkled with its cooking juices.

10) Chicken strips with radicchio

Ingredients:
- Chicken breast 650 g
- 400 g long radicchio
- Brown sugar 30 g
- Water 100 g
- Extra virgin olive oil 10 g

FOR MARINATING
- Extra virgin olive oil 50 g
- Thyme 2 sprigs
- Marjoram 2 sprigs
- Salt up to taste

Take the chicken breast, cut it in half, and make some pretty thin strips. Pour the oil into a pan, add the thyme and marjoram leaves, and season with salt. Distribute the strips of chicken next to each other in the pan so that the marinade is evenly distributed; cover with cling film and refrigerate for at least 2 hours. Wash the radicchio with plenty of fresh running water; remove the base, cut it in half, remove the hard edge, and then cut it into strips lengthwise. In a pan, add the water, the brown sugar and cook for another 2 minutes. Also, add the radicchio cut into strips and cook for 2 minutes, raising the heat. Remove the chicken from the refrigerator and add it to the vegetables. Cook for 2-3 minutes and, when the chicken turns brown, turn off. Finally, you can serve and taste your chicken strips with radicchio.

11) Veal skewers with rocket and scamorza cheese

Ingredients:
- **Slices of veal 600 g**
- **Scamorza 200 g**
- **Rocket 50 g**
- **Extra virgin olive oil q.s.**
- **Salt up to taste**

Detach the rocket leaves from the stem, wash them under running water, and then pat them with a kitchen towel to dry them. Cut the scamorza cheese into thin slices, then beat the veal slices between two sheets of paper. Spread one of the slices of meat on the cutting board, place the slices of smoked cheese on top and cover with the rocket. Roll the meat lengthwise to form a roll. Now insert some skewers inside, which will hold the filling in place and facilitate cutting. Divide the veal roll into 4 parts, gently remove the skewers and reinsert them inside each part. Heat a pan with a few tablespoons of extra virgin olive oil and place the veal skewers inside. Cook them for 7 minutes, turning them halfway through cooking. Add salt and serve your veal skewers with rocket and scamorza.

12) Loin of rabbit mashed carrots

Ingredients:
- **12 rabbit loins**
- **5 carrots**
- **Vegetable broth 2 spoon**
- **Oil**
- **Salt**
- **Vegetable butter 1 teaspoon**

Heat three tablespoons of oil, add the diced carrots and two tablespoons of broth, cook, and add salt. Remove and blend until you have a smooth cream. Heat four tablespoons of oil and a knob of butter, place the rabbit loins in it, brown them evenly, salt them at the end. Remove them and cut each loin into two or three pieces. On the bottom of the serving dish, pour the carrot purée and, on top, the rabbit loins. Serve.

Chapter 9 : Dessert

1) Yogurt dessert with raspberries

Ingredients:
- 500 g of white yogurt
- 180 g of cocoa butter
- 20 g of white almond cream
- 5 tablespoons of rice syrup
- a few pinches of vanilla powder
- the grated zest of 1 organic lemon

To garnish
- chopped pistachios
- fresh raspberries

Combine the yogurt, cocoa butter melted in a bain marie, almond cream, rice syrup, vanilla, and lemon zest in a blender bowl. Work these ingredients at medium speed until you get a soft mixture that you will divide into small molds; put it in the freezer for at least 4 hours. When ready to serve, immerse the base of the containers used in boiling water and turn the sweets on a serving plate. Finish by decorating as you prefer, distributing the washed raspberries and chopped pistachios.

2) Quinoa pralines with peach pulp

Ingredients:
- **1 ripe yellow peach**
- **150 g of quinoa**
- **2 tablespoons of brown sugar**
- **7 tablespoons of coconut flour**
- **5 tablespoons of chopped pistachios**

Peel the peach and chop the pulp in the mixer until you get a homogeneous cream that you will put in the fridge. Rinse the quinoa well under running water and cook it in a pot with boiling water for the package's time. When cooked, drain it, put it in a bowl, add the sugar and let it cool completely. Add with the coconut flour and the peach cream until you get a thick and compact mixture that you will work with your hands to make balls with a diameter of about 3-4 centimeters. Roll them in chopped pistachios and put them in the freezer for 20 minutes, then transfer them to the fridge and always serve them cold.

3) Pear dessert with chocolate sauce

Ingredients:
- 100 g of pitted dates
- 100 g of walnut kernels
- 100 g of peeled hazelnuts
- sea salt
- vanilla powder
- 1 tablespoon of lemon juice
- 1 tablespoon of cocoa butter

For the stuffing
- 420 g of cashews soaked for about 6-7 hours
- 2 ripe pears, peeled and cleaned
- the juice and grated zest of ½ organic lemon
- 160 ml of agave syrup, cooled in the freezer for about 25 minutes
- 100 g of melted cocoa butter
- 70 g of dissolved coconut oil
- 1 tablespoon of white almond cream
- ½ teaspoon of ground cinnamon
- grated nutmeg

To garnish
- 75% melted dark chocolate
- dried pears

Put the agave syrup in the freezer for about 25 minutes. Reduce the walnuts and hazelnuts to a reasonably fine grain in the bowl of a mixer. Leave aside. Start the appliance again and chop the dates you have washed under running water; continue to operate, add the salt, vanilla, lemon juice, and melted cocoa butter. Add the previously chopped dried fruit, and when you have obtained a compact mixture, spread it on the base of a small springform pan (or a loaf pan) lined with baking paper.

Level well using a spatula and put to solidify in the freezer or refrigerator. Now dedicate yourself to the filling. Take the cashews and grind them for a long time in the mixer to obtain a paste. Add the lemon juice and zest, agave syrup, cocoa butter, coconut oil, almond cream, cinnamon, nutmeg, and continue until everything is combined. Stir in the pears, too, to make a soft mixture. Pour it on the well-firmed base and let it cool in the freezer. Remove a few minutes before serving, garnish with melted chocolate and dried pears.

4) Strawberry Tofu Mousse

Ingredients:
- **200 g of natural tofu**
- **250 g of strawberries**
- **3 tablespoons of 100% gluten-free rice or corn malt**
- **chocolate flakes**
- **some mint leaves**
- **1 tablespoon of lemon juice**
- **water as required**

Prepare a mint infusion by leaving the leaves to infuse for at least ten minutes in hot water. Strain it and use that water to boil the tofu together with three tablespoons of malt for a few minutes. After cooking, let the mixture cool in its water to make it flavor well. Drain and blend the tofu with the clean and chopped strawberries and a tablespoon of lemon juice. Use the infusion water to help you combine the tofu and strawberries well and obtain a soft mousse. Pour the cream into the cups and store it in the refrigerator for an hour. Finally, garnish with fresh mint leaves and chocolate flakes.

5)   Lactose-free tiramisu

Ingredients:
- **12 ladyfingers biscuits**
- **80 g of cane sugar**
- **30 g of corn starch**
- **500 ml of rice milk or soy milk**
- **½ vanilla pod**
- **150-200 ml of coffee**
- **dark chocolate**

Lightly beat the egg yolks with the sugar and starch in a bowl. Pour your favorite milk over it after heating it together with the vanilla pod cut in half. Put the mixture back on the heat and heat it, continually stirring with a whisk. As soon as the cream starts to simmer, remove it from the heat and let it cool in a clean bowl, stirring frequently. Quickly dip 6 ladyfingers in the coffee so that they absorb it without breaking, place them gently in a bowl of suitable size and cover them with a layer of custard. Repeat the operation by overlapping the other biscuits and spreading the remaining cream on them. Grate the dark chocolate on the surface of the cake until it is completely coated. Let the tiramisu rest in the fridge for 6 hours before serving it very cold.

6) Quinoa truffles with chocolate

Ingredients:
- 100 g of quinoa
- 200 ml of vegetable milk
- 200 g of almonds
- 100 g of whole cane sugar
- apple juice
- 2 teaspoons of flaked agar-agar
- 2 teaspoons of cocoa powder
- 1 teaspoon of cinnamon
- grated zest of 1 lemon
- 1 teaspoon of cream of tartar

Lightly toast the quinoa without using fat and cook it with sugar and vegetable milk (without using the water). Let it swell and cool. Meanwhile, dissolve the agar-agar in a glass of heated apple juice, then add the lemon zest, cinnamon, and cream of tartar. Stir in the chopped almonds, cocoa, and cereal. Let the mixture cool well and then form truffles with the help of a teaspoon. Bake at 180 degrees for 20 minutes.

7) Coconut and almond cream with ginger and turmeric

Ingredients:
- **280 ml of coconut milk**
- **2 tablespoons of almond butter**
- **2 tablespoons of rice syrup**
- **2 teaspoons of coconut oil**
- **½ teaspoon of powdered ginger**
- **1 teaspoon of turmeric powder**
- **shelled almonds, to decorate**

Combine the milk and coconut oil, almond butter in the bowl of a blender and blend well to mix. Add the rice syrup and ginger and operate again for a couple of minutes. Pour the mixture into individual bowls or glasses, which you will chill in the refrigerator for 4-5 hours. When ready to serve, complete with turmeric powder and chopped almonds. Serve the cream and enjoy it immediately.

8) Chocolate pears

Ingredients:
- **1 kg of pears**
- **a little cinnamon or vanilla**
- **100 g of bitter chocolate**
- **3 tablespoons of honey**

Peel the pears, halve them and remove the core. Put them in a saucepan with cinnamon or vanilla and cook them slightly covered with water. Then transfer them to a serving dish, keeping the cooking water. Melt 3 tablespoons of honey in a saucepan and pour it over the pears. In its place, put the chopped chocolate with a little cooking water from the pears. Let it melt until smooth, adding more cooking water if necessary. Spread it over the pears and serve.

9) Cocoa rice roll

Ingredients:
Ingredients
100 g of rice flour
100 g of quinoa flour
25 g of almond flour
30 g of unsweetened cocoa powder
50 g of maple syrup
70 ml of corn oil
10 g of cream of tartar
30 g of soy sauce cream
100-150 ml of soy milk
a pinch of cinnamon
a pinch of salt

For the rice
150 g of brown rice
150 g of rice malt
400 ml of almond milk
50 g of raisins
50 g of chopped and toasted hazelnuts
40 g of coconut flakes
the grated rind of 1 lemon
1 small teaspoon of cinnamon
1 pinch of salt

Pour the almond milk into a saucepan, add the rice and a pinch of salt. Cook over high heat until boiling, lower the heat to low and without turning cover, allowing the liquid to be absorbed entirely. Add the raisins, the chopped and toasted hazelnuts, the grated lemon peel, the cinnamon, the coconut, and the rice malt: mix well with a wooden spoon allow to cool. Gather the rice, quinoa, and almond flours, the yeast, the bitter cocoa, the salt, and the cinnamon in a bowl. Separately, mix the oil, soy sauce, maple syrup, and 100 ml of soy milk. Pour them into the container with the dry ingredients and work the mixture until it forms a solid and elastic ball (if necessary, add the rest of the soy milk). Let it sit for 20 minutes. With a rolling pin, roll out a pastry by pressing from the center outwards and forming a ½ cm thick rectangle: to prevent the dough from sticking to the pastry board, repeatedly sprinkle with rice flour, rewinding the dough into the rolling pin. Put the pastry obtained on a cloth. With the polish, brush only 2 cm of the rectangle's sides and spread the sweet rice over the entire surface, except the brushed edges. Using the cloth, gently roll up the long side to form a cylinder (be careful not to let the filling come out) and arrange the cake on a baking sheet lined with baking paper. Put the roll in a preheated oven at 200 ° for about 25 minutes. As soon as it is out of the oven, brush with the polish and let it cool.

10) Cups of chocolate and vanilla cream

Ingredients:
- **2 cups of rice or almond milk**
- **4 tablespoons of corn starch**
- **3 tablespoons of rice malt**
- **1 teaspoon of vanilla powder**
- **100 g of bitter chocolate powder**
- **1 pinch of salt**
- **1 piece of lemon peel**

To garnish
- **1 bowl of strawberries**
- **Dried fruit to taste**

Put a little milk in a saucepan, and when cold, melt the starch, stirring vigorously. Take the remaining milk and place it on the fire in another saucepan with a pinch of salt and the lemon peel. When it is about to boil, lower the heat, remove the lemon peel, add the vanilla powder, mix well and finally add the malt. Continue to mix over low heat, mixing the vanilla well and dissolving the malt. Now add the milk previously prepared with starch: raise the heat, bring it back to the boil, and, continuing to stir, remove from the heat. The vanilla cream is ready. Now repeat the same operation with the doses indicated above for the vegan chocolate cream: instead of adding the vanilla, you will incorporate the chocolate powder. Let the two creams cool slightly. Take some dessert glasses or bowls and proceed with the ingredients' layering: start by placing the chocolate cream on the base, alternate the diced strawberries and cover with the vanilla cream, more diced strawberries, and a final layer of chocolate cream. As a decoration, use little strawberries and a handful of toasted and chopped dried fruit, such as almonds, pine nuts, walnuts, hazelnuts.

11) Dark chocolate, almond and matcha mini-cupcakes

Ingredients:
- **200 g of 70% dark chocolate**
- **1 handful of shelled almonds**
- **matcha tea**
- **a few pinches of Himalayan salt**
- **a few pinches of vanilla powder**

Melt the dark chocolate in a double boiler. As soon as it has liquefied, add the chopped or chopped almonds, 2 teaspoons of matcha tea, salt, vanilla, and mix well. Pour the mixture into small molds for chocolates or into muffin molds in which you have inserted cupcake cups. Let it cool to room temperature or in the refrigerator. When the sweets have entirely solidified, decorate them with a sprinkling of matcha tea.

12) Orange cake

Ingredients:
- **300 g of wheat flour 00**
- **150 g of clear raw cane sugar**
- **½ sachet of yeast**
- **the zest and juice of an orange**
- **50 ml of extra virgin olive oil**
- **vanilla sugar to taste**

In a bowl, mix flour, brown sugar, yeast, the grated rind of an orange together with its juice, extra virgin olive oil, and about 100 ml of water. Mix everything with an electric or hand whisk until you get a creamy mixture. Transfer to a pan greased with oil and sprinkled with flour. Bake at 180 degrees for half an hour. When cooked, spread the icing sugar over the cake.

Chapter 10: Sauces, Pesto, Condiments

1) Broccoli pesto

Ingredients:
- 350 g of broccoli
- 50 g of shelled hazelnuts
- 1 tablespoon of cashews
- 1 clove of garlic
- 5 tablespoons of oil
- salt

Clean the broccoli and steam it for about 5-6 minutes. Let it cool, keep the cooking water aside, and purée it in the mixer with the chopped oil seeds and sliced garlic. Complete with oil and salt. If necessary, add a little of the preserved liquid. This cream is ideal for dressing pasta!

2) Fig jam with toasted almonds and lemon

Ingredients:
- 1 kg of figs
- 200 grams of whole cane sugar
- the juice and peel of one lemon
- 15-20 peeled almonds

Wash the figs, cut them into 4, and place them in a bowl covered with sugar, lemon juice, and the peel cut into thin strips and deprived of the white part. Cover and let stand overnight. The next day, cook the jam over high heat for about half an hour. Add the almonds to the mixture, which you have lightly toasted and cut into not too small pieces. Continue to cook until the density reached is not optimal: do not wait for it to become excessively thick, do the test with a spoon; if the jam slips slowly, it is ready to be put in jars. Place it in the sterilized jars up to about 1 cm from the edge, close hermetically, and place them on a wooden cutting board upside down, one next to the other covered by several cloths to conserve heat.

Let it cool, and then turn it upside down.

3)   Lactose-free custard

Ingredients:
- **4 yolks**
- **80 g of cane sugar**
- **30 g of corn starch**
- **500 ml of rice milk or soy milk**
- **½ vanilla pod**

Lightly beat the egg yolks with the sugar and starch in a bowl. Pour your favorite milk over it after heating it together with the vanilla pod cut in half. Put the mixture back on the heat and heat it, continually stirring with a whisk. As soon as the cream starts to simmer, remove it from the heat and let it cool in a clean bowl, stirring frequently.

4)   Homemade mayonnaise

Ingredients:
- **100 grams of natural sugar-free soy yogurt**
- **100 grams of sunflower oil**
- **1 gram of salt**
- **8 grams of lemon juice**

Drain the yogurt of any excess liquid and pour it into the blender together with the lemon and salt. Start the blender and pour the oil slowly for 20 seconds. Your mayonnaise is ready.

5) Eggplant sauce

Ingredients:
- 2 medium-sized eggplants
- 1 clove of garlic
- abundant basil
- parsley
- a pinch of grated lemon zest
- 20 g of pine nuts
- extra virgin olive oil
- sea salt

In a saucepan, bring lightly salted water to a boil. In the meantime, clean, peel and divide the eggplant pulp into chunks. Blanch the eggplants for 3 minutes, then blend them until they are reduced to a smooth and homogeneous cream. Season with salt and season with oil and a small piece of lemon zest. With a mixer's help, prepare an emulsified sauce based on garlic, basil, a few parsley leaves, extra virgin olive oil, and salt. Serve the eggplant sauce with the basil emulsion and the pine nuts toasted in a pan on top.

6) Coconut milk cream

Ingredients:
- Coconut milk 400 ml
- Brown sugar 50 g
- Rice flour 20 g

Start by pouring the sugar and rice flour into a saucepan. Then add the coconut milk a little at a time, continually stirring with a whisk. Place on the heat and continue stirring until you reach the desired density, then move from the heat and continue stirring. Pour the mixture into a bowl. Cover with the cling film and let cool before enjoying your coconut cream.

7) Curry sauce

Ingredients:

- **1 tablespoon of corn starch**

- **0.5 green apple**

- **300 grams of fat-free mayonnaise**

- **salt**

- **1 tablespoon of curry**

- **1 onion**

The curry recipe starts with cutting the apple into cubes. Take a pot with plenty of water and bring it to a boil. Add the diced apple, chopped onion, and a tablespoon of curry. The ratio must always be one tablespoon of curry for 1 dl of water. Add a tablespoon of cornstarch to half a glass of water, add salt and pour into a saucepan. Stir until the sauce becomes creamy. Allow to cool and then mix everything with 300 g of mayonnaise.

8) Anchovy sauce

Ingredients:

- **80 g of anchovy fillets**

- **30 g of pine nuts**

- **1 slice of wholemeal bread**

- **parsley**

- **extra virgin olive oil**

Put the anchovies, pine nuts, chopped bread, parsley, and a drizzle of oil in a blender. Blend until creamy. Your anchovy sauce is ready to be served.

9) Herbal sauce

Ingredients:
- **1 bunch of aromatic herbs**
- **2 tablespoons of extra virgin olive oil**
- **200 ml of light fresh cream**
- **salt**
- **pepper**

First, wash the chosen herbs (I used basil, rosemary, parsley, and mint), dry them, remove the stems, and chop them. Once chopped, put them in a bowl and add salt, pepper, cream, and oil, then emulsify well with a fork. The herb sauce is ready; you can use it immediately or keep it in the fridge.

10) Fresh tomato sauce with basil

Ingredients:
- **Copper tomatoes 1.2 kg**
- **Extra virgin olive oil 3 tbsp**
- **Salt up to taste**
- **Basil 8 leaves**

Remove the stalks and wash them very well, then dry them. Cut each tomato into two halves and remove the green part of each of them' stem. Squeeze the two halves of the tomato into a bowl or sink so that all the seeds come out. Put the tomatoes in a steel pot, which you will arrange on low heat covered by the lid; let the tomatoes cook, turning them from time to time until they are wilted and come apart. Pass the tomatoes with a vegetable mill making the sauce converge in a bowl; once all the tomatoes have been passed, pour the sauce into a smaller steel pot that you will put on the stove. Add the salt and oil to the sauce, consume it over high heat to the desired density, turn off the heat, and add the whole basil or coarsely chopped by hand. Perfect with spaghetti!

11) Guacamole

Ingredients:
- **Ripe avocado 1**
- **Green chilli 1**
- **Copper tomatoes 1**
- **Extra virgin olive oil 20 g**
- **Lime juice 10 g**
- **Shallot 10 g**
- **Black pepper 1 pinch**
- **Salt up to 1 pinch**

Start by looking after the avocado. Cut it in half lengthwise, then sink the knife's blade into the core and pull to extract it easily. Cut the pulp with a small knife to remove it more easily with a spoon; collect it in a small bowl. Then cut the lime in half and squeeze it to obtain the juice, be poured on the avocado pulp; Then, season with salt and pepper, and mash the pulp with a fork. Set aside, then peel and finely chop the shallot, then wash, dry, and slice the tomato: obtained from the cubes' slices. Then tick the green (or red) chili pepper, empty it of its seeds, cut it into strips, and then into cubes. Then in the bowl with the crushed avocado pulp, pour the chopped shallot and the diced tomatoes. Also, add the chili and oil, stir and add more salt and pepper if necessary. Your guacamole sauce is ready to be enjoyed!

12) Sauce at nuts

Ingredients:
- **Walnuts 160 g (shelled and without peel)**
- **Extra virgin olive oil 70 g**
- **1 clove garlic**
- **Pine nuts 20 g**
- **Parmesan to be grated 30 g**
- **Whole milk 160 g**
- **Marjoram 4 g**
- **Bread crumb 30 g**

Take a bowl with high sides and pour the breadcrumbs to which you will add the milk. Mix the crumb with the milk so that it can moisten well. When the breadcrumbs have softened, pour the bowl with the bread over a tightly meshed colander placed on a small bowl to drain the excess milk and, if necessary, press lightly with a spatula. Collect the extra milk and set aside. Now take the walnuts, then add them in a mixer with bread previously soaked in milk and pine nuts. Then add garlic, marjoram, and grated cheese. Operate the blender and gradually add the oil and the milk kept aside to make your walnut sauce more creamy and thicker. Season with salt and pepper. When you have obtained a nice homogeneous mixture, your walnut sauce will be ready to flavor dishes!

Conclusion

Rheumatoid arthritis is a chronic inflammatory disease, potentially disabling systemic, with an etiology not clearly defined but probably of autoimmune origin. The disease mainly symmetrically affects the joints, but being systemic can involve many organs of the body, such as the heart, lung, and kidneys.

Symptoms commonly associated with rheumatoid arthritis affect the joint sites affected by the disease and include swelling, warmth, pain, stiffness, especially in the morning, and limited movement. The extra-articular manifestations, which we will discuss in the rest of the article, are also important.

Rheumatoid arthritis is two to three times more frequent in women than in men and, in general, occurs between the ages of 40 and 60; however, it can start earlier or later. It affects about 1% of the American population each year; it is less common than arthrosis, a disease typical of aging that causes progressive wear of the articular cartilages.

There is no definitive cure, even if many behaviors have been observed that can improve symptoms and slow pathological progress; let's see which ones:

Diet: To be sure, it is still uncertain whether certain specific dietary measures have a genuinely positive effect; on the other hand, there is a real nutritional strategy to reduce joint inflammation.

 Regular Exercise: Recommended for maintaining muscle strength and general physical function; however, exercise fatigue helps to decentralize attention from localized pain. Despite the pain, it is strongly inadvisable to interrupt various occupational activities (of daily life).

Printed in Great Britain
by Amazon

78374245R00063